THE
TABLOID
SHAKESPEARE

THE
TABLOID
SHAKESPEARE

Nick Page

HarperCollins*Publishers*

HarperCollins*Publishers*
77–85 Fulham Palace Road, London W6 8JB

First published in Great Britain in 1999 by
HarperCollins*Publishers*

1 2 3 4 5 6 7 8 9 10

The illustrations of Cleopatra and Juliet which appear on
pp. 13 and 140 are used by kind permission of Louisa Hare,
First Folio Cards. © 1995, 1997 Louisa Hare.

Nick Page asserts the moral right to be
identified as the author of this work

A catalogue record for this book is
available from the British Library

ISBN 000 274053 2

Printed and bound in Great Britain by
Woolnough Bookbinding Ltd, Irthlingborough, Northamptonshire

The Bard

FOR CAESAR JOLLY GOOD FELLOW

Triumphant Julius Returns to Rome

Citizens decked the streets with laurel as Caesar returned to Rome today, after an impressive victory against Pompey's army.

Crowds mobbed his tour bus as it drove through the Roman streets. Thousands chanted his name and called for him to be crowned.

"Who cares about the republic?" said one ecstatic fan. "We want him to be King."

Sceptics

Others, however, were less well disposed.

"No one can deny that he's achieved a great victory," said Cassius, a lean and hungry bystander. "But we mustn't get things out of proportion. This country has a long tradition of republicanism."

Caesar himself has been denying rumours of impending royalty.

"We have no intention of becoming King," he said. "We would be very satisfied with just being a minor deity, or household god. And we'd like to wear a crown. And sit on a throne. But as to being a King, no way."

Despite his success on the away leg, there are rumours that many Senators are not happy with his ambitions. But stories of a split have been played down by fellow Senator Brutus.

"Julius has the complete confidence of us all," he said. "We're right behind him. Literally."

Dear Cassandra

The Bard's Mystic Answers Your Questions

Dear Cassandra,
I have recently had some dreams about my husband.

I dreamt that his statue was pouring forth blood and a load of Romans were washing their hands in it. Then a voice said, "Beware the Ides of March," a large warning light started flashing on and off and a black cat ran across my path shouting "Don't go to the Senate!"

Finally, a marching band walked by playing a song called "Caesar's going to get it in the neck".

I am sure it means something, but what?
Yours Mrs J.C.

Dear Mrs J.C.
I have consulted a dream interpreter who says that your dream shows you have a morbid fear of becoming an estate agent.

There is really nothing to worry about. I suggest eating less strong cheese and getting out more. You need a bit of fresh air. Why not go for a walk with your husband through the streets? After all, you're not likely to get stabbed or anything, are you?

With warm forebodings
Cassandra

If you wish to see Cassandra's prognostications, either write to The Bard, or pick up one of the cards in the telephone kiosks.

Weather report

There will be unsettled weather tonight, with thunder, lightning, people bursting into flames, lions giving birth in the streets, and owls hooting.

Other than that, the temperature will be mild for the Ides of March.

IT LIES IN THE STARS

Leading Citizens' Horoscopes By Madame Osiris

Brutus once claimed that "the fault lies not in our stars, but in ourselves". So what do the stars hold for the main players in today's Rome?

In a unique forecast, The Bard's own soothsayer Madame Osiris reveals all.

Brutus

Star Sign: Libra
Lucky Stone: Gall
With Mars descending and Taurus in a china shop, you will have a decisive day. Remember – he who hesitates is lost.

Antony

Star Sign: Gemini
Lucky Stone: Mick Jagger
Your star is in the ascendant, with Orion's Belt just over Orion's trousers and Capricorn in Uranus. Just don't push your luck too far. Avoid anything Egyptian.

Caesar

Star Sign: Aries
Lucky Disease: Measles
Good for you! With Pluto ascending and Donald Duck falling over you may die laughing today. I'm not saying you're doomed, but it might be best not to start any complicated jigsaw puzzles.

WHAT A PLOT WE'VE GOT!

Caesar Assassinated By Former Supporters

Julius Caesar was assassinated today as he walked from his house to the Senate.

A group of assassins set upon him as he walked from his home "Dun Conquering" to take his place in the Senate House.

"He was stabbed in the colosseum," said Detective Inspector Marcus Humungus. "Which, as anyone will tell you, is a nasty way to go."

His assassins have been identified as former colleagues Brutus, Cassius, Cinna and some others. In a statement tonight they claim to have acted on principle.

"Caesar was getting too big for his boots," said one of the conspirators. "He was aiming to be King. So it's not so much a stabbing, more a demotion."

Lieutenant

Meanwhile, Mark Antony, Caesar's trusty lieutenant, has strongly condemned the murder.

"He was a great man," he said. "I am devastated by his death."

Others have claimed that Mark Antony is making political capital from the death and is over-reacting.

"I don't know how they can say that!" he sobbed, tearing his hair, ripping his toga and rolling around in agony on the carpet. "I'm deeply upset! I intend to make a speech tonight about it in the Senate. I shall in particular be calling on all fishmongers to 'Cry haddock, and let slip the cods of war!' "

Vacuum

Caesar's death leaves behind a large power vacuum. Not to mention three mops, a floorbrush and a large feather duster. Political commentators are predicting an imminent power struggle. The sides are lining up, with the conspirators against Mark Antony and Caesar's nephew, Octavius.

"There's going to be a blood bath," said one senator. "It'll all end in tears, you mark my words."

EAR EAR!
Mark Antony In Dramatic Lughole Loan Plea

BARD EXCLUSIVE

Mark Antony won a tense TV debate last night – despite a baffling request for parts of the audience's anatomy. "Lend me your ears!" he cried at one point, much to the concern of the studio audience.

"We all looked at each other and wondered what he was on about," said one listener. "I think he was speaking metaphorically, but one old bloke threw his wooden leg at him."

Despite this bizarre request, Mark Antony won the TV debate with Brutus hands down.

"He was impassioned, articulate and persuasive," said one teenager. "He kept telling us that Brutus was an honourable man. But it sounded more like he was putting Brutus down than anything else."

After the broadcast fans rioted and the conspirators' party were forced to flee through a back door. War now seems inevitable between the two sides.

THE BARD SAYS

There have been many rumours about Caesar's political ambitions.

Some said he wanted to be Emperor. Some said he wanted to be King. A few even thought he wanted to be Queen.

He bestrode this narrow world like a colossus. Which was OK providing you didn't look up. But now this mighty man is dead.

Brutus claims that he acted for the good of Rome. That Caesar acted as if he was above the law.

But what is assassination if not "above the law"? Isn't assassination the weapon of tyrants?

Hasn't Brutus acted just like Caesar himself?

Rest assured, we will not bow before tyranny. This paper will remain impartial, objective and honest.

That is why we believe Mark Antony is the man for Rome. He has honesty. He has integrity. Most of all, he has a gang of trained thugs standing outside the door of our offices.

The Bard. The paper that's not afraid to praise great political leaders with names that rhyme with Hark Mantony.

MARK ANTONY'S SPEECH, FIRST DRAFT

EXCLUSIVE

In An Exclusive Scoop, The Bard Has Obtained A Leaked Copy Of Antony's First Draft

Friends, Romans, Countrymen, ~~Welsh~~, lend me your (ears.)

Surely you mean 'tears'?

'come to bury'?

I bum to cury Caesar, not to praise him.

The evil that men do lives after them, the good is oft interred with their bones. ~~But that's life.~~

The noble Brutus hath told you that Caesar was ambitious. (But then Brutus is a big fat pooey head who couldn't run the country for toffee, so there.) *A bit more mature here, perhaps?*

You all did love him once, not without cause, What cause witholds you then to mourn for him? O judgement thou art fled to (british breasts.) *brutish beasts?*

And men have lost their reason.

TEARS!

If you have (ears) prepare to shed them now. This was his mantle. See what a rent the envious Casca made, through this the well-beloved Brutus stabbed. Mark how the blood of Caesar followed, as if rushing out of doors for a fag. *not v. poetic, is it?*

This was the most unkindest cut of all - ~~apart from that accident I had with the garden shears when I was six.~~ For when the noble Caesar saw him stab, he was really (really annoyed.) *stronger*

And so, take arms my friends, else the ghost of Caesar will himself rise up and speaking thus 'Cry Paddock!' and let slip the ~~Donkeys~~ of war. *dogs*

change - Haddock? fanny Craddock?

Lots of Love, M.A.
Tony *Don't like ending - needs a bit more pizazz. Is there a will knocking about? If not, why not?*

ONE LUMP OR TWO ?

Brutus's Wife Dies In Bizarre Coal Eating Episode

The armies are lining up for tomorrow's battle. Meanwhile it has been revealed that Portia, the wife of Brutus, has died in a bizarre fire-eating accident.

"She swallowed two burning coals and choked to death," said a horrified family retainer. "I think she had a premonition that Brutus is going to lose. Either that or she was attempting to eat the world's hottest curry."

Others claim it was all an accident.

"Perhaps she just wanted a coke, and someone made a clerical error," said a servant.

Ghosts

There are rumours that in the rebels' camp all is not well. Brutus and Cassius have fallen out over tactics and servants report that Brutus has not been sleeping.

"As a stoic, he took the news of his wife's death very calmly," said Lucius, a servant. "But in the middle of the night he started crying out and muttering about 'Philippi'. He looked like he'd seen a ghost."

BRUTUS BEATEN

Cassius Dead. Brutus Dead. Bodies Everywhere

The battle of Philippi has been lost by the rebel alliance. Brutus, Cassius and their forces staked everything on a last throw of the dice but were cut to pieces by a superior army.

And in the aftermath of the battle both Brutus and Cassius were found slain. Both had committed suicide rather than be captured.

"It's always difficult telling what happened in a battle," said a source. "But it certainly looked like a very bad communications error."

Mistake

Cassius is reported to have killed himself when he thought that his best friend Titinius had been slain.

"He saw Titinius surrounded and heard a cry and thought he was slain," said his servant Pindarus, who is now in hiding. "Then Titinius came back and found Cassius dead so he topped himself. It's just been a horrible mix up really. Still, you've got to laugh."

When Brutus found out he was very upset.

"He was really cut up," said his servant Strato. "Although not as much as Cassius, obviously."

Lost

Brutus returned to the fray, but without Cassius the day was lost. In the end, Brutus killed himself rather than be taken.

"It's a tragedy, really," said Mark Antony, standing over the body. "Everyone else in the conspiracy hated Caesar. But Brutus really believed he was acting on noble motives. Ah well, it's an ill wind and all that."

Mark Anthony is expected to take control of Rome for the forseeable future.

BARD BABE

© 1995 Louisa Hare

Now that's what we call a Queen!

Cleopatra (36-30-34) is all woman, as several Roman Emperors have found out. This gorgeous Nile-babe is rich, powerful, beautiful, alluring. And she has some of the biggest pyramids you've ever seen!

Not only that, but she's a big hit with the animals, as you can see from the asp (2-2-2) that is crawling over her chest.

"I've always been fond of powerful beasts," she says. "Crocodiles, desert lions, Julius Caesar, you know the sort of thing."

Now Cleo is looking for a long-term relationship.

"I want to settle down," she says. "I'd like to meet a man, fall in love, found a dynasty and start several futile wars."

The Bard says – she can invade us any time!

CLEO
A Tale Of Tragedy

They called her the most beautiful woman in the world.
They were the world's most famous couple.
Everywhere they went, crowds gathered, the paparazzi drew their hieroglyphics, reporters carved their stories.
They shone in the sky like two shiny glow worms. Big shiny glow worms. Big shiny glow worms with powerful torches.
Now, in this collector's special, you can read their story...

1: Cleo Barges In

"That woman knows how to make an entrance," said Enobarbus, Antony's long time friend.

"When he first met her, he was in the royal barge. It was magnificent. Huge, purple sails, silver oars and a golden poop. I've never seen anything as magnificent as Cleopatra's enormous poop."

The boat carried spices and perfumes which wafted across the air.

"It was incredible," continued Enobarbus. "I mean, if you were downwind of this thing, you knew it was coming. It was like a huge, floating air-freshener. Everywhere she went she was accompanied by exotic smells. She is the original spice girl."

Antony was sitting in the town square, expecting to receive a tribute from the Queen. Instead he had to go to see her.

"He was completely upstaged," confirmed Enobarbus. "And from the moment he saw her, it was love at first sight. At least on his side. She looked like a cat who'd caught a mouse. I didn't know whether she was going to kill him, or toy with him. Still, what a poop."

2: No Place Like Rome

Antony's wife, desperate to get him back, even resorted to leading an army against Caesar.

"I think she hoped Antony would come to her aid," said her marriage guidance counsellor. "As cries for help go, launching an invasion is a pretty big one. Unfortunately she was killed, so it kind of backfired."

It wasn't until Pompey's attack on Caesar that Antony was roused to action. He returned home to Rome and there he "came to his senses", marrying again. But not Cleopatra; Caesar's sister Octavia.

"You must understand that the alliance was in danger of falling apart," said Agrippa, who brokered the deal. "By marrying Octavia, Antony pledged allegiance to Caesar again. It was a political marriage. But it is true to say that Antony was a different man in Rome. Away from that woman, he was more stable, more boring. Let's face it, more Roman.

"He went to Rome for peace, but he went to Egypt for pleasure. She was beautiful, wilful, sensuous, infuriating and she played a mean game of billiards."

3: Call Of The Nile

It was not long, however, before Antony grew disillusioned in Rome.

Soon Antony was back in Egypt. And this time there was no turning back.

"He and Cleo sat in the market place at Alexandria," said a servant. "Right next to Abdul's Fruit and Veg Stall. Their chairs were solid gold. At their feet sat Caesarion, the son of Cleopatra and Julius Caesar. He had his own special seating place – a sort of Caesarion section."

Antony put together an alliance to fight Caesar, including kings such as Bocchus of Libya, Archelaus of Cappadocia, Adallus of Thrace, Lawrence of Arabia, Flagon of the Medes, and Kevin of Essex.

TONY
iumph And Togas

4: Lost At Sea

From the start it was a disaster.
"It was madness," said Enobarbus. "Caesar had bigger ships, better sailors and much nicer uniforms. His ships were so fast. I think all the oarsmen had been on extra Weetabix."

The battle started well. Then Cleopatra, who was commanding one of the ships, took fright. She turned her ship round and fled. Antony immediately turned and followed her.

"It made me sick," said Enobarbus. "Never in his life had he run away from anything. But here he was chasing this woman like a wounded duck. He could have stayed, but he ran. They had their chance, but they threw it away."

5: One Treaty And She's Anybody's

Following their defeat, Caesar sent Thidius to Egypt to tell them that he would have mercy on one condition: that Cleopatra leave Antony and take up with him.
"The amazing thing is she actually agreed," said Thidius. "Mind you, she'd knocked about a bit. First Julius Caesar, then Gnaeus Pompey, then Mark Antony. She was the ultimate groupie really."

For her part, Cleopatra claimed that she was only playing for time.

"Anyway," said a palace source, "Let's be fair here. Antony didn't hesitate to marry Octavia when it suited him. What's sauce for the goose is sauce for the gander and all that."

6: Final Throw Of The Dice

Although Antony won the first part of the final battle, once again he was let down as the Egyptian fleet deserted to Caesar. In his rage, he blamed Cleopatra. He even threatened to kill her.
Cleopatra was frightened. She fled to her monument, a semi-detached pyramid on the outskirts of the Valley of Kings. Then she sent a messenger to tell Antony that she was dead.

"I don't know what she hoped this would achieve," said the messenger. "She told me to tell him her last word was 'Antony'. Not very believable, if you ask me. I mean, most people's last words are 'aaarghhh.' "

Antony decided to do away with himself and fell on his own sword. Unfortunately, he missed.

"It was only then that Cleopatra realized her plan wasn't the most sensible," said Diomedes. "She sent word to tell Antony that she was still alive. Typically she left it that little bit too late."

8: A Pain In The Asp

Antony was taken on a stretcher to where Cleopatra was hiding and there he died.
"When Caesar heard that Antony was dead, he sent word that Cleopatra would be welcome to live in Rome," said Proculeius, one of Caesar's officers. "She would have had her own bungalow, nice little used chariot, all the creature comforts. I guess it's hard to retire when you've been Queen of all Egypt."

"She knew what would happen," said Dolabella, an emissary from Caesar. "She knew it would mean being mocked and ridiculed and, worse than all that, getting old. We didn't think she'd top herself. When Abdul the fruit and veg man arrived with a basket of figs we thought she had a touch of constipation or something."

But the fig basket contained two deadly asps. Cleopatra applied the first asp to her breast and the second to her arm.

"They were big snakes," said Dolabella. "It looked like she had three arms. I couldn't tell her asp from her elbow."

Caesar arrived to find her dead, with her two attendants. Forensic evidence convinced him that the asps had committed the crime. He ordered her to be taken and buried alongside her Antony.

As Caesar said, "No grave upon the earth shall clip in it a pair so famous."

Their story was both glorious and pitiful at the same time. Love was both their ruin and their glory.

"They were no good for one another, but they couldn't bear to be apart," said Dolabella. "If love is a drug, then these were the worst addicts I have ever seen."

The asps were sentenced to thirty years.

GIVE US OUR DAILY BREAD

Storehouses Crammed With Grain
Interest Rates Soaring
New Laws Punish The Poor
We say, enough is enough!
The Bard – The Paper of the Proles

Enough is enough.
That's the message from the increasingly desperate proletariat filling Rome's streets.

"The Senators are doing nothing," said one citizen. "They sit in the Capitol and stuff their faces while we starve. We demand action."

Their mutterings have met with little sympathy from the Senate.

"They are the scum of the earth," said Caius Marcius. "If I had my way I'd behead them, shoot them in the kneecaps, chop out their bile ducts and feed them to the crows, burn them to ashes and then ask them to leave the country."

"I don't think he likes us much," said an onlooker. "He's not exactly what you'd call a man of the people, is he?"

Luckily for the people, Caius Marcius has been called away to fight the Volsces.

"This is what we need," he said. "A good bit of mindless slaughter and brutality. Bring back hanging, that's what I say."

Volsces on the March

Once again the Volsces are marching against Rome.
"I don't know why they keep doing it," said a spokesman. "They've attacked loads of times and each time Caius Marcius has defeated them.

"Like my old Dad used to say, if at first you don't succeed, use bribery."

BARD SPORTS

All the Action
All the Time

CALL ME CORIOLANUS

Caius Marcius Accepts New Title

He's the undisputed champion
He's beaten the best
Caius Marcius is dead. Long live Coriolanus!

After an epic battle swinging one way and then the other, Caius Marcius defeated Aufidius and the Volsces at Corioli yesterday.

"The fight was a real ding-dong battle," said our battle correspondent Harry Mechanical. "The early rounds went to Aufidius. Marcius took some brutal blows and was cut. But his corner patched him up and he carried on."

Force

He came back from the ropes, swinging hard, punching with frightening force. Aufidius, who thought he had the fight won, saw his championship slipping away from him. Five times he has met with Marcius, five times he's lost.

"I'm the greatest," said Marcius. "I'm the best. There's no one better than me. I float like a butterfly and sting like a bee with a flipping great sword."

Honour

Now Marcius has been given a new honour by a grateful people.

"He will be called Coriolanus, in honour of this great victory," said a grateful senator. "It's the least we can do." However, the newly styled 'Coriolanus' rejected the thanks of the crowd.

"I don't want your gratitude," he said. "I'm the best."

"The least he could do was say 'thank you'," said a source. "He's not only the best fighter, he's got the biggest head as well."

ELECTION SPECIAL
Consulships Decided
Coriolanus Defeated

Coriolanus has been defeated in his attempt to become Consul. He was rejected by a populace who could not stomach his pride.

When asked if he had a message for the people all he would say was, "Bid them wash their faces and keep their teeth clean."

"Whilst this is no doubt excellent health advice," said one commentator, "we were really looking for something a bit more inspiring."

"His trouble is that he does not love the common people," said a disgruntled voter. "I don't care if he did save Rome from the Volsces. I'm not having him as Consul and that's that."

The argument flared at a meeting that should have seen Coriolanus installed as Consul. Instead an angry mob rejected him.

"I fought for my country," shouted Coriolanus. "I deserve a bit better." This comment fell on deaf ears.

"Just because a bloke bashes another bloke doesn't make him a good Consul," said a citizen. "A big sword is no basis for executive power."

The election speech descended into chaos with Coriolanus accused of treason and having to fight his way out of the hall.

CORIO-LEAVE-US!
Coriolanus Banished From Rome

Following nights of rioting and mob rule, Coriolanus has been banished from Rome.

"All he managed to do was put people's backs up," said a source. "His presence was inciting civil unrest. He had to go."

Coriolanus had only recently faced a charge of treason, which he vehemently denied. Nevertheless, it gave his enemies enough ammunition to exile him from Rome forever.

"I don't know where he will go," said the source. "But without an army he's nothing."

HE'S BACK – AND THIS TIME IT'S PERSONAL

Coriolanus Returns At The Head Of An Army

Rome Under Siege As Ex-hero Wreaks Revenge

Coriolanus has returned to Rome at the head of the Volscean army. He has already destroyed most of the Roman forces. Now many outlying regions have joined his army.

"He leads them like a thing made by some other deity than nature," said Cominius, one of the few to stand against his banishment. "The deity responsible for 'Psychopathic murders' springs to mind.

"Our daughters are raped, our roofs melted, our women dishonoured. I think you could say he's a bit miffed."

Even now, his army camps outside the walls, preparing to destroy the city.

"We should never have banished him," said a Senator. "I mean, alright, so he was an arrogant killing machine with nothing but contempt for ordinary people. But nobody's perfect."

LISTEN WITH MOTHER

Coriolanus Retreats After Appeal From His Mum

"He's A Good Boy, Really," Says Volumnia

Coriolanus has retreated from Rome following a last-minute appeal by his mother. She met the invading general outside the walls of Rome.

"I suggested to him that he could be the one to bring about peace between the Volsces and the Romans," said Volumnia.

"I know he appears a bit hard at times, but he's a big softie underneath it all. I've still got his cuddly teddy-bear at home. Well, actually it was a cuddly great white shark, but the principle's the same."

Volumnia was accompanied by Coriolanus' wife Virgilia and their son Eric Marcius Junior.

"We knew he wouldn't really attack us," said his wife. "Well, we were pretty sure he wouldn't anyway. Actually, now I come to think about it, we weren't certain at all. Still, he's always listened to his mother. She's the only person more frightening than he is."

Victory

"My mother has won a great victory for Rome," said Coriolanus in a press conference. "I realized that I couldn't destroy my home town, not after her appeals. It was her love that swayed me. That and the fact she told me Father Christmas wouldn't bring me anything in the future if I was a naughty boy."

Instructions

The news will come as a bitter blow to Aufidius, leader of the Volsces. After years of being defeated by Coriolanus he has now been defeated by Coriolanus's mum as well.

"I gave Coriolanus strict instructions to destroy Rome," he said. "Naturally he must do what he thinks best. When he returns I will have several points to put to him. All of them wielded by large assassins."

LEAR TODAY, GONERIL TOMOR-ROW!

Crazy King In Kingdom Giveaway

Daughters Divided As The Realm Is Split

In an astonishing decision, King Lear has literally given away his kingdom.

"Basically, the King felt it was time to hand over the reins," said a palace spokesman.

"He wanted to shake the cares and business from his age. And let's face it, at his age you're often physically unable to do the business."

But the decision led to a bitter split between his daughters, Goneril, Regan and Cordelia.

Love

The King decided to give the largest part of his Kingdom to whichever daughter loved him the most. However, his youngest daughter, Cordelia, refused to say anything. She has since been banished to France, a large country near Paris.

"She'll be OK," said one of her women-in-waiting. "The King of France fancies her and the wine is a lot cheaper over there."

Kent

The Earl of Kent has also been banished after trying to turn the King from this course of action.

"He said the King was mad," said a witness, "which is slander. I mean, it's true, but it's also slander."

The King is now embarking on a tour of the country, along with a retinue of one hundred knights, quite a lot of horses and a dog. He will, as ever, be accompanied by his faithful fool.

"Nay and thou canst not smile as the wind sits, thou'lt catch cold shortly," said the fool.

"That's a cracker," he added.

GLOUCE-STER IS CHEESED OFF
Son Flees Father's Rage

Edgar, son of the Duke of Gloucester, has fled after his father uncovered a plot against his life.

The Duke believes that Edgar was plotting to kill him. The evidence was in a letter thrown through the window of Edmund, the Duke's illegitimate son.

"Naturally, my father is very upset about this," said Edmund. "I can't understand why my brother would plot against my father."

Others have pointed out that Edmund has benefited from this change of events.

"If you ask me, that letter was a forgery," said a source. "I mean, it was written in crayon for one thing. And it talked about 'The Duck of Gloster' which doesn't smack of an educated man."

"Something is not right, here," said an insider. "But Gloucester's rage has blinded him to all the arguments."

NO MORE DAD'S ARMY
Regan And Goneril Deny Their Dad

Ex-King Lear has been expelled by his daughters and forced to cut his retinue in half.

"It's a very painful thing to do," said an aide. "It brought tears to his eyes. He had a very big retinue, after all."

The Queens objected to their father's assumption that they would still look after him.

"I don't mind him having a few friends round," said Queen Goneril. "But one hundred knights is far too many. As I've always said, once a knight is enough for anyone."

Stormy

Lear left Goneril in a temper and went to his other daughter, Regan. However, he fared no better there. In the end he stormed out into a storm.

"I think he needs to knock at the portcullis and ask for Lord Reality," said Regan. "Both my sister and I agreed that he could stay here with us, but there's no need to have all those trappings of kingship around any more. After all, he isn't a king. He's just a silly old man."

Wilderness

The King is rumoured to have fled out into the wilderness accompanied only by his fool.

"It's bad enough being out on that blasted heath in this weather," said an onlooker, "But to have to listen to the fool's jokes as well. It's enough to send anyone mad."

BLIND LOYALTY

Gloucester Loses His Eyes In Punishment For Helping The King

The Duck of Gloster* has been blinded after he tried to help the exiled King Lear.

"I am sure my father is grateful for this merciful sentence," said his bastard son, Edmund.

"It could have been much worse. I'm not sure how, exactly, but it could have been."

Crime

Gloucester's "crime" was to take the old King into his castle and offer him shelter.

"The Duke has done nothing wrong," said a servant. "He found Lear in a hovel on the heath. The King was soaking wet and freezing cold. He was sheltering from the storm with his fool, a servant looking remarkably like the ex-Duke of Kent, and a complete nutter called Poor Tom. It must have been hell out there."

Savage

Gloucester's part in this plot was revealed to Goneril and Regan by Edmund. The two Queens were furious, not only that Lear was given shelter but that he was then allowed to escape.

In a savage attack, Regan and her husband, Cornwall, blinded the old man and threw him out of his castle to fend for himself.

"They didn't even give him a guide dog or anything," said an eye-witness. Or an "eye-removal witness" to be more specific.

Concern

The Queens claim that they were merely concerned for their father's safety.

"We wanted to 'look after' our Dad," said Goneril. "He's not coping on his own. He'd be happier with us."

"That's happier spelt D-E-A-D," said a servant. "Regan and Goneril are bad news. I blame it on their names, personally. If you sound like a B-movie actor and a sexually transmitted disease, then it's bound to sour your view of life."

Dover

No one knows where King Lear has gone, but the rumours are that the King has fled towards Dover.

"I don't know why he's gone there," said an observer. "There's nowhere he can go beyond that. Unless he builds a tunnel or something."

* Sorry, Duke of Gloucester

DEFEATED IN VICTORY

Albany Wins But Everybody Still Snuffs It

In the small hours of yesterday morning, the army, led by Albany and Edmund, defeated the invading French led by Lear's estranged daughter Cordelia.

However the day ended in tragedy with Lear and his daughters dead.

"Goneril poisoned Regan to get her hands on Edmund," said an observer. "But Edmund was killed by his brother Edgar – using his stage name of Poor Tom. Goneril couldn't take it, and stabbed herself."

Cordelia

Unfortunately, Edmund had given an order to have Cordelia hanged. And he died before he could rescind it. Albany sent an order reprieving her, but the messenger arrived too late.

"It's a tragedy, but orders are orders," said a guard. "We just couldn't process the paperwork quickly enough. She was strung up by red tape."

Her death proved too much for the ex-King, who died with his faithful daughter in his arms.

Death

"I think at the end he was back to his mad old self," said Kent. "He thought that Cordelia was still alive. It was the shock of his joy that killed him, not the grief."

"He was the victim of his own foolishness and lack of judgement," said a political commentator. "There's a difference between 'old' and 'mature'. Unfortunately, he never worked out what it was. Ripeness, as they say, is all."

Ask Aunty Albion

Advice from the wise old woman in woad...

Dear Aunty Albion,
For some time I have been pretending to be a lunatic called Mad Tom. I did it because I was in hiding after my father suspected me of trying to murder him. Anyway, I recently met my father, who is now blind, having been thrown out of his own castle.

Unfortunately, following his eye-removal, Dad now wants to throw himself off the white cliffs of Dover.

Naturally, I do not want him to do this. Not only because he is my father, but because I don't think the 'white-with-a-big-splotch-of-pink cliffs of Dover' has quite the same ring to it.
How do I stop him jumping?
Yours
Poor Tom
  PS I suspect that my half brother is a bastard in every possible sense of the word.

Dear Poor Tom
Well, you could take him to the top of a very flat hill and let him jump. That might cure him and then you could both share a jolly good laugh at this hilarious practical joke.

Alternatively you could let him jump. After all, life's not exactly a bed of roses for you lot is it?
Best wishes, Aunty Albion

INTO THE WOODS

Courting Couples Elope To Avoid Arranged Marriage

Helena and Lysander have run to the woods to avoid being married to other people.

Helena was offered a choice. Marry Demetrius and lose the man she loved. Or become a nun. Strangely, she chose to elope.

"I don't know what's going to become of her," moaned her father Egeus. "Everyone knows those woods are dangerous. She'll probably get eaten by a load of teddy-bears or something."

Followed

The couple have been followed by Demetrius, the jilted fiancé, and Helena's friend Hermia, who is secretly in love with Demetrius.

"It all sounds like the plot of a very bad farce," said a forestry commission official. "All I hope is that they don't light any fires. This is the height of midsummer after all."

IS THERE A MONSTER IN THOSE WOODS?

"I Saw His Ears", Say Horrified Actors

A group of actors today reported the presence in the woods of a mysterious half-man, half-donkey.

"It was enormous," said Peter Quince, a carpenter and amateur actor. "It had a great, fat, wobbly body and the head of a donkey. As if that wasn't hideous enough, it was a really bad actor."

Disappearance

The mystery is deepened by the disappearance of one of the leading actors of the troupe. Nick Bottom, the weaver, disappeared in the woods while the group were rehearsing a play for the wedding celebrations of the King.

"We're still not sure what has happened to him," said Quince. "I just hope he hasn't made an ass of himself."

COULD IT BE REAL?

An Expert Reports

Many people have claimed to see monsters.

They are the stuff of legend – the Loch Ness Monster, the Abominable Snowman, Jeremy Beadle. All horrific creations of mankind's darkest imaginings.

Now we have the Athens Ass, the half-man, half-donkey that is terrorizing the woods at night.

These halflings are not unusual in human myth. There have been many creatures who are a mixture of human and animal, such as the centaur, the mermaid, or Buffalo Bill. What makes this creature different is that so many people report having seen it.

Will it turn out to be a hoax? Or a new species? Only time will tell.

What is certain is that mankind needs these inventions. We need to know that there are fairies at the bottom of our garden. Or even in the woods.

Police Crack-Down On All-Night Raves

Following reports of strange disturbances in the woods outside Athens, police have vowed to crack down on all-night parties.

"We have had several complaints from neighbours about the noise," said an inspector. "It appears that the Fairies have been up all night playing tricks and generally making a racket. This is anti-social behaviour and should be stamped out."

Police are also investigating drugs found near various trees.

"We have taken possession of a number of substances," confirmed the inspector. "Including some nectar, a number of herbs and something called 'Mistress Quickly's Snogamatic Love Potion'. I think it's some kind of ecstasy substitute."

TRIPLE BILL
All Go For The Wedding of the Year

The bells rang out. The confetti was thrown. The chickens were ritually sacrificed. Athens celebrated as the triple wedding finally took place.

King Theseus married his Amazon bride, Queen Hippolyta. And they were accompanied in their nuptials by two other weddings, Demetrius and Helena, and Lysander and Hermia.

"It all worked out perfectly in the end," said Demetrius, who only twenty-four hours before wanted to marry somebody else. "I went for a long walk in the woods and when I came out I wanted to marry Helena. It's funny, I never saw her qualities before. But now I think she's gorgeous."

The brides were wearing ivory silk togas with matching tiaras and floral head-dresses. Hippolyta's outfit was further set off by her six foot long bow and the shrivelled head of one of her enemies dangling from her garter.

"Well, she is an Amazon after all," said her designer. "At least we persuaded her to leave the broadsword at home and take the razor blades off the chariot wheels."

After the ceremony, all three couples were off to the West End to take in a show.

"I'm very relieved," said Philostrates, the master of the revels and organizer of the show. "At one stage we had one couple definitely marrying, one couple eloping, the other two not speaking to each other, and a mad donkey loose in the woods. It could have been a disaster. But it's turned out to be a wonderful dream."

FOR HE'S A JOLLY GOOD OTHELLO!

Desdemona Marries Othello On Moonlit Flit

Desdemona, daughter of Senator Brabantio, has married General Othello after a daring moonlight elopement.

The General, who is supreme commander of the Allied Forces, said they were "very much in love." He didn't think their different races an obstacle.

"I know that I am a Moor and some people hold that against me," he said. "But I think we're all a bit more enlightened now. After all, if I'm good enough to die for Venice, surely I'm good enough to marry a Venetian?"

Reservations

Senator Brabantio, however, has expressed reservations.

"No-one," he told us, "could call me a racist. But if you ask me, I think he's cast some kind of spell on her. They do that sort of thing you know.

"It's obviously voodoo. How else would you explain the fact that she has turned down all the wealthy curled darlings of our nation?"

Dangers

Othello dismissed the claims.

"She loved me for the dangers I have passed," he told us. "I showed her my decorations and my medals. She was particularly impressed with the size of my gongs."

War News

The news comes as Venice prepares to fight against the Turks. The Ottomans have invaded Cyprus and General Othello will be leading the assault against the enemy's forces. The signs are that the Duke will try to

clear the matter up quickly, so that he can send Othello to war.

"Naturally, if Desdemona says that she married Othello of her own free will, then I will approve of the match," confirmed Brabantio. "However, until I hear it from her own lips, I have to assume that he has given her some kind of love potion. Or possibly played a Barry White record, which I believe has the same effect."

Othello, meanwhile is preparing to embark.

"I will leave my wife in the care of my servant Iago," he said. "It's good to have someone you can trust in these matters."

Iago was unavailable for comment.

HANKY-PANKY!

Has The Moor's Missus Blown Her Nose With Another?

Dramatic new evidence has been sent to the offices of The Bard, indicating that Desdemona (20), the wife of General Othello (35), has been leaving her linen in someone else's linen-basket.

She has given a treasured handkerchief to Michael Cassio. The handkerchief was a present from her husband, Othello.

"It was a very special treasure," said an anonymous source. "It reminded her of the time they both had a cold. It's incredible to think that she would have given it to someone else."

Temper

According to sources, the General lost his temper in a furious row with his wife. "It meant a lot to the general. It was his mother's. I've never seen anyone so het up over a Kleenex."

"He accused her of all manner of things," said our source. "He called her a whore and an impudent trumpet. Sorry, strumpet. I tell you, that man has the temper of a grizzly bear with PMT."

Iago was unavailable for comment.

Cassio Loses His Pips

Drunken Brawl Leads to Dismissal

Cassio, lieutenant to Othello, has been stripped of his commission — after being discovered in a drunken brawl.

"This is not the kind of responsible behaviour I expect from a senior officer," thundered the Moor.

"I'm afraid we're going to have to tear his epaulettes off."

Innocence

Cassio, meanwhile, protested his innocence.

"I've been set up!" he exclaimed. "Someone got me drunk, I just can't remember who."

When informed that he would lose his commission, a badly hung over Cassio said.

"I don't care. Do anything you want, just don't shout while you're doing it."

Iago was unavailable for comment.

MOOR'S THE PITY!
Othello In Wife-Murder Scandal

Othello, the chief of armed forces, has murdered his wife Desdemona, in a furious attack.

The crime took place following a series of allegations that Desdemona had been conducting an affair with Cassio.

The deed was interrupted by her servant Emilia, who was too late to save her mistress.

"With her last breath she denied that Othello had killed her," said an anonymous source. "But he admitted it straight out. He loved not wisely, but too well. Or at least, not bad for a beginner."

Unstable

An anonymous source said that Othello had been unstable for years.

"He always had a terrible temper," he said. "And he was prone to fits as well. I ask you, is that someone who should have been leading our armed forces?"

Events at the scene of the crime are confused so far, but early reports indicate that Iago's wife, Emilia has also been killed.

Iago was unavailable for comment.

WHY DID THIS TRAGEDY HAPPEN?
An expert writes...

It's a funny thing, tragedy

(Technically speaking, of course, comedy is meant to be funnier, but anyone who has listened to Launcelot Gobbo, Feste the Clown or any of those idiots will know that they are far more depressing than any known tragedy. But I digress.)

Who knows where the roots of tragedy lie?

The Greeks had a word for it: Kebab.

Unfortunately the word means "hot sandwich made of strangely conical sheep", which doesn't quite capture the essence.

Tragedy Begins At Home

No, all tragedy begins with us. We all have a fatal flaw. Something that pushes us just that little bit too far.

With some it is ambition. With others it is indecision. For Othello it was jealousy.

Be My Downfall

And when it gets out of control, it leads inevitably to our downfall.

If it could have been controlled, then none of this would have happened. Tragedy is always "accidental".

But that's what makes it so tragic.

THE BARD
A statement

The Bard is a paper of record. We have a long and noble history of reporting the facts.

That is why we feel we need to respond to these latest charges.

We have been accused of misrepresenting the truth.

We have been accused of "chequebook journalism", of paying money to anonymous sources for information.

We have even been accused of being manipulated by evil men for their own ends.

Naturally we refute these arguments.

In the light of the revelations from the so-called Othello case we feel we need to make our position clear.

At no point did we give Iago money for his so-called information.

Jewels, yes. Costly ointments, lotions, precious spices and Nubian slaves certainly. But cash, no.

It has been revealed that Iago set up the whole thing, creating a tissue of lies which caused Othello to murder Desdemona.

It has been insinuated that The Bard has been a pawn in this game.

We are no man's pawn. We simply reported the facts. Is it our fault the big bloke couldn't control himself? Is it the fault of the media when people take us too seriously?

This is a tragedy, there is no denying it. But, in order that there should be no more recurrence of this type of thing – not that we accept responsibility – we have drawn up a new code of conduct.

- We will no longer use engravings from the paparazzi.
- We will not report on scandal or gossip unless sales absolutely demand it.
- We will continue to uphold the highest standards of journalism as we understand them.
- We will only report on people's private lives where issues of the public interest are at stake (always remembering that the public are really, really interested in this sort of thing).

We believe that we owe it to the memory of Desdemona and Othello to make these pledges. We will continue to report the news with dignity, restraint and good taste.

BARD ADVICE
Find Your Fate With the Weird Sisters — Medusa, Morgana and Gladys

Dear Witches,
I am a simple Thane, but my wife is always on about our future and how great things are ahead of us. Can you tell me what will happen? And should I trust you further than I can throw you?
Yours,
Mr M., Thane of Cawdor.

Dear Mr M.,
We have prognosticated. But Gladys cleaned it up with a mop.
  Your future is what you make it. You could be King, or it could be the Thane as always.
  Take it into your own hands. You will be Thane of Glamis, we know it. And King? Who can say? It could be you.
  And yes, that is a dagger you see before you.

Dear Weirdies,
I am looking for a place to stay the night.
  Someone has suggested to me Dunsinane would be a nice place. The air is healthy and the temple-haunting martlet flits about like nobody's business.
  But I don't know, I get this sort of creepy feeling about it. Can you help me?
Yours,
Duncan of Scotland.

Dear Duncan,
Go ahead, enjoy yourself. These are your friends. Just don't ask for room service.

Dear Sisters Three,
My son and I are having an argument. I say he should train to be an accountant, but he says he is probably going to be bloodily murdered by an assassin along with his sisters and brothers, and possibly myself. Can you help me to get through to him?
Yours,
Mrs MacDuff

Dear Mrs MacDuff,
By all means start your son training to be an accountant. After all, if he does get brutally murdered it will come as a welcome relief.

Dear Medusa, Morgana and Gladys,
I wonder if you can help me. I have always felt that my mother never loved me. I think it was because I was from her womb untimely ripped. That and the fact she called me Brian. Also I have this urge to carry branches about with me. Can you help?
Brian

Dear Brian,
Don't worry, your mother loves you. But have you thought about taking out some life insurance on your family recently?

Send your letters to:
The Weird Sisters
Just Behind the Cauldron
A Small Cave
The Outer Hebrides

DUNCAN DONE-IN

King Killed By Drunken Guards Macbeth Made Monarch

In a terrible tragedy, King Duncan has been found murdered in his bed. He was stabbed to death by a drunken guard – who was in turn slain by Macbeth.

"I just couldn't help myself," said Macbeth. "I mean, he was standing there looking all innocent. But he had 'guilty' written all over his face. In biro."

Innocent

The tragedy comes fast on the heels of the King's victory against the rebels. His sons, Malcolm and Donalbain, have been implicated in the murder.

"Of courses everyone is innocent until proven guilty," said Macbeth. "But the fact that they fled doesn't look too good for them, does it?"

Haggard

Lady Macbeth appeared at the press conference haggard and distraught.

"This is an appalling thing to happen under our roof," she said. "Apart from anything else the laundry bills are going to be horrendous. I never knew old men had so much blood in them."

When asked how she would like to be Queen, she just smiled and said, "I will do my best. But first I want a wash."

BANQUO AT THE BANQUET

A royal feast, held in honour of King Macbeth was disrupted tonight when he claimed to see visions.

"You cannot say that I did it," he yelled at one point. "Never shake thy gory locks at me!"

Onlookers didn't know who he was talking about.

"I thought he was talking to me at first," said one serving wench. "I know my hair needs a wash, but 'gory' is a bit much."

But it appeared that the King was having some kind of premonition. Banquo, his best friend, didn't appear at the banquet. He was later found dead in a ditch, apparently attacked by robbers.

"It's spooky," said an onlooker. "It's almost as if the King knew something was going to happen. You don't think..."

Death

Relations between the King and his former fighting partner had cooled lately. Some suspect that the King had a hand in the death of Duncan.

"It's certainly been a meteoric rise to power," said a close friend, the Thane of Thithelthroth. "But I don't think the King is enjoying his job very much. He doesn't look too healthy if you ask me."

DUNCANGATE!
The phone call the King doesn't want us to hear

Yes It's Here – The Transcript The Palace Tried To Ban

This telephone call, between Macbeth and his personal spiritual advisers, was intercepted by a retired shipping clerk from Aberdeen. It shows a King who is depressed, suicidal, and so desperate he is prepared to talk to a load of old witches. It's another piece of evidence in the scandal they are calling "Duncangate".
Phone rings. It is answered.

Macbeth: Hello? Hello? Is there anybody there?

Witch 1: When shall we three meet again?

Witch 2: In thunder, lightning or in rain?

Witch 3: How about Tuesday?

Witch 1: By the pricking of my thumbs, somebody is on the extension.

Macbeth: It's me, you old fool. I must know, will I be King hereafter?

Witch 1: King?

Macbeth: Yes.

Witch 2: King you say?

Macbeth: Yes, I did say King.

Witch 3: So you want to know if you will be King, eh?

Macbeth: YES YOU STUPID OLD WOMEN... (calming down) I am just trying to find out my future.

Witch 1: You'll have to cross our palms with silver.

Macbeth: How am I going to do that over the phone?

Witch 2: Well, at least give us your credit card details.

Macbeth: I've already got an account with you.

Witch 2: I'm just cutting open the chicken right now. Oh no, I don't believe it!

Macbeth: What is it? What's wrong?

Witch 3: No giblets! The cat will be upset. He loves his giblets.

Macbeth: But what does it say?

Witch 2: You will be King, until Birnam Wood comes to Dunsinane.

Witch 1: Or it could be Borehamwood.

Witch 3: No, it's definitely Birnam Wood.

Macbeth: And shall a wood come to Dunsinane? I should cocoa.

Witch 2: Wait, there's more.

Macbeth: What now?

Witch 1: It says here that no man born of woman will ever kill you.

Macbeth: No man born of woman? But that means, I'm invincible!

Witch 2: Not necessarily. I mean you could get trampled to death by an okapi.

Macbeth: In Scotland?

Witch 2: A long shot, I grant you, but stranger things have happened.

Witch 3: Anyway, never mind all this, how are you feeling in yourself? Are you still having the visions?

Macbeth: Yes. The other day I thought I saw a dagger before me. Thankfully it was only the loofah otherwise I might have done myself a nasty injury. And life is very boring.

Witch 2: You don't sound yourself.

Macbeth: No. My life is fallen into the sear, the yellow leaf.

Witch 1: Is it that bad?

Macbeth: Tomorrow and tomorrow and tomorrow, creeps on this petty pace until the third stroke of recorded time.

Witch 3: You want to get out more.

Macbeth: Life is a tale, told by an idiot, full of sound and fury, signifying nothing.

Witch 1: Still, you've got to laugh, haven't you?

At this point the recording ends.

DISH OF THE DAY
Ragout Of Newt

As cooked by the Weird Sisters on their TV programme
Ready, Steady, Prognosticate

Ingredients

1 eye of newt – peeled
1 toe of frog
Wool of bat – 300 gm
1 dog's tongue
1 goat's gall bladder
Entrails of a small tiger (*only available at selected Chinese food suppliers*)
2 eggs
A pinch of mandragora
Lizard's leg
Slow-worm's sting
Curry powder (optional)
Nose of a Turk
Lips of a Tartar
Liver of a blaspheming Jew (omit if cooking for vegetarians)
Preheat a large cauldron to Flipping Hot.

Put all the ingredients into the pre-heated cauldron. Add 2 litres of fetid water from a poisoned well. Stir well and simmer over a low pyre for 4 hours, chanting all the time. Every now and then stop and drool over the pot in a disgusting, semi-senile way.

After three hours, call on Hecate, spirit of the underworld and dark god of all Scottish food, to bless the pot. Simmer gently for another 10 minutes. Cool the mixture with baboon's blood.

Serve with bashed neeps and plenty of shortbread.

This recipe tastes appalling, but will give you the ability to see into the future, sink ships thousands of miles away and listen to the bagpipes without any ill-effects.

WOOD YOU BELIEVE IT!
Forest Comes To Dunsinane

There was chaos on the one-way system outside Dunsinane today when a large wood appeared out of nowhere.

The wood (452) had been transplanted and carried by the invading army of Macduff and Malcolm.

"We wanted to disguise ourselves," said a large tree, which later turned out to be Malcolm. "So we thought we would carry a bit of foliage."

"Let's face it, it's not much of a disguise is it?" said one soldier, who had carried a rather well-established sycamore for hundreds of miles. "I mean, the purpose of disguise is not to let the enemy know you're there. He looks out one morning and suddenly sees a huge forest in his front garden, he's bound to be a bit suspicious."

King Macbeth, against whom the army is marching remains unperturbed. "I don't care," he said. *"Even if it was Birnam Wood, it doesn't matter. No natural-born man can ever kill me."*

Nevertheless, he looked nervous as he scanned the newly arrived foliage.

"There aren't any okapis in there are there?" he asked.

BARD SPORTS

All the Action All the Time

THE BIG FIGHT
Macduff Versus Macbeth For The All-Scotland Tyrannical King Title

Our man at the ringside, Wee Jock McStrap

This was the big one. The rumble in the jungle. (Well, the wood, at least.) The fight in the night. The rattlement on the battlement.

At the weigh-in Macbeth was almost trance-like, his eyes uncaring and dark.

"He's had a bad week," said the promoter, Warwick the Kingmaker. "Lady Macbeth died yesterday."

Macbeth shrugged. "She should have died hereafter," he said. "Or possibly Wednesday."

His opponent, however, was alert and alive, although still removing some of the twigs from his clothes.

"This man is a killer," he said of Macbeth. "He killed Duncan. He killed Banquo. He killed my chicks. This is judgement day."

Calm

When the fight began, Macbeth looked cool, calm and relaxed, as if he knew he couldn't be beaten.

Macduff, tense, like a coiled spring. Suppressing his rage. Controlling his aggression.

They circled each other warily, until Macduff whipped out his claymore.

The crowd gasped.

He struck Macbeth once, twice, thrice, er... fource, but the blows glanced off the King's upturned shield.

The King retaliated by aiming some short slashing blows to the sporran.

End of round one: honours even.

Taunts

As the bell went for round two, Macbeth began to taunt his opponent.

"You can't kill me, son," he said. "Give up now. Put your claymore away."

But Macduff ignored him. Instead he launched another furious onslaught which the wily, experienced King parried with his sword.

Macduff was looking tired now. His claymore had been whittled down to little more than a toothpick. He threw it away and reached into his sock where he kept his dirk.

"You can't kill me," taunted the King. "No man born of woman can ever kill me."

Ripp'd

It was then that Macduff released his hammer blow.

"I was not naturally born," he snarled. "I was from my mother's womb untimely ripp'd. And anyway, my mother was an okapi."

That was the point where everyone at ringside heard the sound of the King's bottle smashing. He lost it completely. The colour drained from his face.

"Lay on then Macduff," he said. "And cursed be he who fails to strut their stuff!"

Oblivion

Macduff struck quickly. A jab, a hook, a left to right slash and the King was down. Before the bell could save him, Macduff's sword took the old King on a one-way ticket to oblivion. Or, at least, Stockport.

He went down as he had lived: pretty depressed really.

The fight was over. Yet no-one who witnessed it will ever forget the pictures. Macduff, his claymore whirling round his head, ablaze with vengeance.

Macbeth, despairing and defeated. Knowing that his time was up.

Two men in kilts, whacking lumps out of each other.

Now that's what I call tragedy!

PHILIP THE LION-CUB

Son Of Coeur-de-lion Is Knighted

In a dispute at court, King John has knighted the illegitimate son of his absent elder brother, Richard.

The boy, Philip Faulconbridge, was born after an affair between Richard and Lady Faulconbridge. They took their chance when Richard sent Lord Faulconbridge abroad as an emissary.

"I think my father suspected something when my brother was born only five and a half months after he came back. My Mum tried to claim he was early. But since he weighed 10lb, she was obviously lying."

Minstrels

"Of course the surprise is that Richard fathered anyone," said a courtier, who declined to be named. "We never knew he was into that sort of thing at all. He spent most of his time down the Crusaders' Club, hanging out with his minstrel, if you know what I mean."

Philip and his brother Robert were brought before the King in a dispute over inheritance. John was so impressed with the boy that he immediately renamed him Sir Philip and adopted him into the Plantagenet family.

Surprise

"We were very surprised at John recognizing the bastard son," said a source. "But then again, it's probably a case of it takes one to know one."

Lady F. admits affair

In a tense press-conference today, Lady Faulconbridge admitted having a passionate affair with King Richard.

"By a long and vehement suit I was seduc'd," she said. "Frankly, he treated me like one of his sieges. It was a war of attrition."

The revelation decides the recent argument over Philip's parentage.

"Oh Richard was the father, all right," said Lady Faulconbridge. *"He may have had the heart of a lion, but he had the manners of a baboon."*

A LOAD OF PAPAL BULL!

John Excommunicated

OI JOHN, GET A NEW RULER!
Calls For King To Step Down In Favour Of Nephew

Philip of France has called for King John to step down in favour of his nephew, Prince Arthur.

"Arthur is the rightful heir," he said. "His unnatural uncle has usurped the throne. And I intend to put things right."

"Obviously I'm not doing this for personal gain. No, really, I'm not. I'm just being a good European partner."

The King was speaking at a press conference which was also attended by the Archduke of Austria, the man who is widely credited with the death of Richard the Lion-heart.

Siege

Now the French-Austrian alliance are besieging Angiers, trying to get the English forces to retreat.

"I will not retreat and I will not abdicate," said John. "I have just as much right to the throne as he does. Anyway, I got here first."

Nevertheless, the King is willing to make concessions.

"If he likes, he can be Duke of Brittany," he offered. "It's a lovely place and he'll never be stuck for somewhere to go on holiday."

Pope wants to choose Bishop

King John has been excommunicated by Pope Innocent. It follows his refusal to accept the Pope's nominee as Archbishop of Canterbury.

The Pope demanded that Stephen Langton, the King's chosen archbishop, stand down.

"His holiness has the final say on this issue," said the Commissioner for Ecclesiastical Affairs, Pandulph. "There is a clear European directive on the appointment of Archbishops."

Beef Ban

"This really is intolerable," said a furious King John. "First they besiege our towns, now they are trying to choose our archbishops. They'll be banning our beef and forcing their currency on us next."

In revenge for the way he has been treated, the King has ordered Philip the bastard to return to England and extort money from the church.

"Might as well be hung for a sheep as for a lamb," he explained.

Cont. on page 38

From page 37

Isolation

Despite the King's anger, the move leaves him increasingly isolated in Europe. France has reopened hostilities, the Vatican has issued a formal order of excommunication and our entry for the Eurovision Song Contest has been scrapped.

What is more, King John looks set to come under increasing pressure from the Europhiles within his Dukes and Vassals. They are already unhappy at the way young Arthur Plantagenet has been sidelined.

Despite these setbacks King John remains determined to hold on to his monarchy. "I will not be swayed," said a defiant King. "We fight on. We fight to win."

Do You Think King John is doing a good job?

Or do you think he's just a nobody who should be dispatched with a sharp knife?

Call The Bard's Magna Carta phone poll now!

• Dial 01 to limit the power of the monarchy, enshrine the constitutional rights of the Barons and create the first, limited step towards a modern democracy

• Dial 02 to carry on as we are in a welter of in-bred chinless wonders murdering each other.

It's up to you!

I'M JUST A FALL GUY!

Hubert Blamed For Death Of Prince Arthur

"I Was Set Up!" He Claims

Prince Arthur is dead. In a tragic accident he died leaping from the battlements of the castle where he was imprisoned.

Hubert de Burgh has been jailed for his death. Now, in a Bard exclusive, he claims he was set up.

"King John put me up to it," he told us. "I was given an order to put the boy's eyes out with hot pokers. But as I talked to him I couldn't murder the little angel. I left him safe and sound. He must have taken it into his head to try to escape. Although why he couldn't dig a tunnel like any ordinary prisoner is beyond me."

Forgeries

Hubert has copies of papers from the King, ordering the death of his little nephew. The King, however, is furiously denying the story.

"They're obviously forgeries!" he stormed. "I would never order such a thing. All right, I might have sometimes wished the boy dead. But let us remember that he was a little, golden curled angelic creature, prone to singing merry songs and skipping around. It's only natural to want someone like that to fall under a bus."

Disintegrating

The tragedy is the final straw in the disintegrating relationship between John and his barons. Already Pembroke and Salisbury have withdrawn their support and the King has been forced to make peace with the Pope. Meanwhile French forces have landed in Kent and are seeking to overthrow the King.

"All this is just a ploy to divide us," claimed John. "I'm not a well man," complained the King. "I have a fever. We must pull together against a common enemy."

Hubert, meanwhile was preparing his defence.

"I tell you, I'm a patsy," he said. "I've been set up for this, just because I've got a silly name. But I'm not taking a fall like Arthur did. I'm innocent and I can prove it."

JOHN'S GONE!

BARD EXCLUSIVE

The King Dies, Poisoned By A Monk

King John died yesterday, poisoned by a monk in a revenge attack for taking all their wealth.

"It looks like a straightforward revenge killing," said Lord Salisbury, the chief investigating officer. "You mustn't forget he'd been ransacking the abbeys like there was no tomorrow. Which in his case was absolutely true."

Victory

The King died on the day that the French forces were routed and driven from the land. The French had initially made an alliance with the rebellious Lords, but the Lords turned when they discovered that the French planned to assassinate them after the battle.

"Nobody is going to abolish the Lords while I'm around," said Pembroke, one of the former rebels. "All this business has only served to show what a great institution the hereditary peerage is. I mean, where else would you get a complete nutter on the throne? It's that kind of thing that makes England great."

Turmoil

The death of the monarch brings to an end a reign of turmoil, dissension and political unrest. His son, Prince Henry (23), has been proclaimed King and is already promising changes.

"I'm going to make sure that we don't lose touch again," he promised. "I want a new monarchy. Closer to the people, modern, and less likely to put anyone's eyes out with branding irons. Apart from anyone who really annoys me, of course."

GET LOST, FLIPPER! Dauphin defeated

The Dauphin – French for Dolphin – has been thwarted in his plans to invade England.

Egged on by Pope Devious III, the large sea creature invaded France and made a pact with the rebel alliance.

However, they soon struck back when they discovered his evil plans to betray them.

"No one is going to turn us to the dark side," said the leader of the rebel alliance. "Especially not some big grey fish."

"I am not a fish," said the Dauphin, as he sailed back to France.

"I am an aquatic mammal."

The BARD Probe...
GIRLS WILL BE BOYS

A Bard Special On The Cross-dressing Craze That Is Sweeping Society

CASE 1: CESARIO

"It's like you can't fall in love with anyone these days without demanding to check their birth certificate," said Duke Orsino.

"There are girls pretending to be boys. Boys pretending to be girls. Grown men pretending to be donkeys. It's a pile-up on the gender freeway."

Orsino himself was duped by Viola, who disguised herself as his servant Cesario.

"I should have asked for references when I took him on," said the Duke. "I thought the lad looked a bit of a jessie, but that rather suited my purposes."

The Duke asked Cesario to plead his case to Olivia, an heiress in Illyria.

"It was all going OK until Olivia fell in love with the boy," said the Duke. "That led to all kind of complications, I can tell you."

At one stage Olivia even married Cesario, or rather her twin brother Sebastian who had suddenly appeared.

"What I don't understand is why she had to disguise herself in the first place," said the Duke. "I mean she looked much better with her clothes off. If you see what I mean."

CASE 2: GANYMEDE

"I fell in love with him," sobbed a distraught Phebe (19). This simple shepherd girl from the forest of Arden was duped by the person she only knew as "Ganymede".

"I met him in a glade in the forest," explained Phebe. "I mean, it's hard to see in there sometimes. I just thought there was something different about him. I noticed his chest was a bit larger than others, but he told me he'd been working out."

But Phebe wasn't the only one that Ganymede fooled. Oliver de Boys even used the boy as "wooing practice", unaware that Ganymede was the woman he loved in disguise.

"I must admit I felt a bit cheated," he said. "I practised all my best chat-up lines on Ganymede". He was completely oblivious to the fact that it was his beloved Rosalind in drag. "I thought she looked familiar, but it's difficult to tell when there's so much foliage about."

In the end the confusion was sorted out and the couple were married.

"All's well that ends well," said Orlando. "Oh no, hang on, wrong play..."

Music may well be the food of love, but do you know the true gender of the bloke who is twanging your banjo?
In a special PROBE report for today's, brilliant Bard, we look at the girls who find it more fun to be guys.

CASE 3: FIDELE

"He called himself Fidele," said Polydore, who with his brother Cadwall was a hunter in the wilds of Wales. "I thought there was something odd about him when we met. He was far too good looking for a lad. Still, when you've lived in a cave all your life, you take things at face value."

When Fidele took ill and died, the boys were heartbroken.

"We were devastated," said Cadwall. "Although we'd only known him for a few days, there seemed to be this bond between us. We even composed a song about him. In the end we called it 'Fear No More', which was an improvement on its original title of 'Why have you stopped breathing, you idiot?' "

"I've released it on my own record label," said Polydore.

In the end, Fidele turned out to be the boy's long-lost sister.

"It was a big shock," said Cadwall. "We turned out to be princes and she was our sister. I know it turned out well, but it still isn't right.

"We don't do that kind of thing in Milford Haven."

CASE 4: BALTHAZAR

"It was the most amazing professional impersonation I have ever seen," said Antonio, who discovered that his legal aid barrister was called "Balthazar".

"She was defending me in a Venice bankruptcy case," continued the merchant. "If it had gone wrong I would have been made to look very silly. Not to mention dead."

Amazingly, Balthazar turned out to be Portia, who had just got engaged to Antonio's friend Bassanio.

"Since I lent Bassanio the money to help him marry Portia, I suppose she owed me a favour."

"Naturally we don't approve of this kind of thing," said a spokesman for the Venetian Law Society. "It takes many years of study and a huge amount of money to become a barrister. Not to mention joining the masons and buying all the official clobber. What are all our customers going to think if rich bored housewives start taking it on themselves to go and win cases? I can see our profits falling dramatically."

Originally the Law Society were going to sue Portia for impersonating a barrister, but then they decided against it.

"We thought she might represent herself," said their spokesman. *"And she's a brilliant lawyer."*

Have you ever been fooled by a cross-dressing woman?
Or do you suspect that your true love is actually an accountant called Roger?
Then write to The Bard and let us tell everyone your shameful secret.
Write to:
"My significant other has lumps in all the wrong places"
The Bard, A Rock, The Seashore, Illyria

LOST AT SEA
Royal Passengers Feared Drowned

The Duke of Milan and the King of Naples are among passengers feared drowned in a typhoon.

The tempest, which seemed to centre on a small Mediterranean island, struck during the night, taking the ship and all passengers with it.

"We're baffled," said the Milan weather centre. "The storm seemed to spring up out of nowhere. We haven't seen this kind of weather since the old Duke practised magic fifteen years ago. He was always mucking about with the weather."

Conference

Their boat – the *S.S. Oh-Hell-I've-Dropped-The-Champagne** – was taking them to an important conference on "The Hereditary Peerage and How to Jump The Queue", at which the Duke was to be a speaker.

"It's a terrible tragedy," said a court spokesman. "To think that all those years ago his brother and niece were lost at sea and now the same thing has happened to him. If I were a member of his family I wouldn't go anywhere near boats in the future."

* This is what happens when you get a Scottish goalkeeper to perform the the launching ceremony

MY HOLIDAY DISASTER

Steward Stephano thought he was getting a holiday cruise... instead he found himself marooned!

"It was a nightmare," said Stephano. "I was looking forward to the Mediterranean cruise when the ship went down with all hands. Not to mention legs and everything else as well."

After washing ashore, Stephano immediately contacted the company rep, a half-human, half-fish monster.

"The rep was useless," said Stephano. "He said he wanted to serve me, but he only got drunk. And then we started hearing these voices and fell into a bog. He promised to get us some new clothes but when we got them, we were attacked by spirits disguised as dogs."

"I'm a bundle of nerves," he said. "I'm on a lot of medication. But I'm taking water with it as well."

Negligence

Milan Tours Inc., the company who set up the cruise, deny they have been negligent.

"The man is obviously raving," said a spokesman. "For a start we don't have a rep on that island. And is it our fault if a magical storm suddenly starts up? We've offered him a book token, but he's determined to sue."

Furious

But Stephano is not the only disgruntled customer on the island.

"We're furious," said Alonso, who was shipwrecked on the other side. "We've been attacked by invisible spirits and then when we sat down to the evening meal, it was just taken away from us. Call that service? Because I don't."

The tour party have contacted AITA, the Association of Italian Travel Agents, but without luck.

"I'm afraid our bond scheme doesn't cover acts of revenge by powerful magicians," they said.

ARIEL'S NOT BIOLOGICAL!

Island Helper Is A Magical Spirit

A mysterious magician has been accused of discriminating against non-humans.

"I'm working all hours," said Ariel, the Spirit (346). "I never get a day off. Just because I'm not a biological being, he thinks he can do what he wants. It's discrimination against non-human ethereal beings."

The Spirit is launching a campaign against such discrimination.

"I've started an organization called 'Spirits Against Derogatory and Discriminatory Offences'. Or SADDO for short."

They are already calling for changes.

"For a start, we don't like the use of the word 'spirit'," said Ariel. "We prefer the term 'differently bodied'."

Debt

His employer, Prospero (55), argues that Ariel owes him a huge debt.

"I found the lad trapped in a tree by his previous owner, the witch Sycorax," explained Prospero, the mysterious magician. "You'd think he'd be grateful, after twelve years stuck in a bit of knotty pine. I could always put him back if he wants."

Freedom

However, Ariel is asking for his freedom.

"I want to be free," said Ariel. "I want to make my own choices. I want to wear flares. I am not a number. I am a free man."

"He's getting ideas above his station," said Prospero. "I sent him down the shops the other day and he took four hours and spent my change on beer."

Ariel has received unexpected support from Prospero's own daughter, Miranda (19).

"I think Daddy's being a bit mean," she said. "He's getting a bit obsessed by all this revenge stuff."

Spirit Rights

A SADDO Manifesto

We believe the following rights should be guaranteed to all differently bodied beings:

- Free speech
- Free movement
- Free Nelson Mandela
- Free love (this is more a hope than a demand)
- A maximum 40 hour week, with no ship rebuilding or magic banquets on Sundays
- No more songs with "hey nonny nonny" or "fol-di-ree" in them
- Lower the age of dematerialization to 250

CRIMINALS NEVER PROSPERO!

Miranda in Monster Assault Ordeal

Miranda, daughter of Prospero, has revealed how she was assaulted by a hideously deformed monster called Caliban.

The attack occurred while she was teaching him English.

"He crept up behind my back and grabbed me in the middle of the declensions," she sobbed. "Needless to say, I won't be entering him for his GCSE exam now."

Caliban, however, is unrepentant.

"This is all a fit-up," he snarled. "This used to be my island – my mother owned it. They've taken it from me and now they treat me like a criminal."

Trial

There have been claims that the trial was rigged, especially since the judge was the victim's dad.

"I am nothing if not fair," he argued. "It was an open and shut case. My fair, fragrant, beautiful daughter was assaulted by this poisonous, lying, offspring of a witch and heaven knows what else. Not that I'm biased."

Critics argue that Prospero's treatment of Caliban is motivated by his own bigotry.

"Racism is endemic in the justice system of this island," said Caliban. "I'm a victim of a crypto-fascist, colonial dictatorship. The only reason they haven't got rid of me altogether is that there would be no one left to make the fire and do the washing up."

Caliban plans to appeal.

NO MORE MAGIC

Prospero Gives Up The Spells And Is Reconciled With His Brother

Prospero the magus is to give up magic for good.

"It is time to retire from this rough magic," he told a reporter. "I'm going to break my staff, drop my magic book into the ocean, and take up gardening."

His decision comes after a dramatic reconciliation with Antonio, Sebastian and Alonso, the plotters who originally removed him from the Dukedom of Milan.

"Now my charms are all o'erthrown," he continued. "What I do from now on, I do in my own strength. As long as they give me somewhere with a stairlift I'll be OK."

Return

Prospero will return to Milan, along with his daughter Miranda.

"I can't believe how beautiful people are," said Miranda. "I mean, I've only ever seen myself and my father – and he's no oil painting, I can tell you. But all these wonders awaiting me, all these beautiful people. And they tell me that there are even more in something called *Hello!* magazine."

Reunion

There was a tearful reunion too for Antonio, who thought his son Ferdinand was lost at sea.

"I discovered he was still alive, and playing chess with Miranda," he said. "I was amazed on two counts – first that he'd survived the storm, second that he is intelligent enough to play chess. The only time I played him he thought you had to throw a six to start."

The Bard Classifieds

SITUATIONS VACANT

EXPERIENCED KING REQ'D. Own assassins an advantage. Scotland.

ACTORS URG REQ'D. Rude mechanicals preferred. Ability not necessary.

GARDENERS REQ'D. Must be able to moralize and draw political metaphors.

CLOWNS NEEDED. Must have own hat with bells on and inflatable bladder on a stick. Sense of humour an advantage, although judging by some of the past employees, not strictly necessary. Must be prepared to sleep rough on a blasted heath.

SOLDIERS REQ'D. No slackers please. Must be willing to work on St. Crispin's Day.

VESTAL VIRGINS REQ'D. No experience nec. In fact, the less experience the better.

GRAVEDIGGERS REQ'D. Must be able to put up with Princes interfering. Severe dislike of clowns an advantage.

FINANCIAL OPPORTUNITIES

BLACKMAIL YOUR FRIENDS FOR FUN AND PROFIT – This new book from Iago Publishing tells you how! You too can create tragic situations for your own amusement and even make money from your hobby!

MAKE MONEY AS A MODEL Can you keep still for up to 16 years? Then you, too, could make money this winter as a living statue.

HAVE YOU EVER WANTED TO KEEP ASPS? The ideal family pet. Also good for suicides if necessary. Write to Big Abdul's Asp Emporium.

FOR SALE

HORSE – One horsepower engine; 40 miles on one tank of hay, not needed due to late delivery. Apply Richard III.

LOVE POTION – Hardly used. Works on humans, fairies, donkeys, etc.

STATELY BARGE – One lady owner. Gold throne, perfumed sails, enormous poop. Power assisted rowing.

SHALL I COMPARE THEE TO A SUMMER'S DAY? Poems written, verses rhymed, dark ladies seduced. Call Sonnets-R-Us.

DEATH POTION Play dead with this amazing potion. Fool your family and friends. Watch and laugh as they prepare an expensive funeral. (Not suitable for adolescents.)

CONFUSED BY IDENTICAL TWINS AND THEIR SERVANTS? Use Slappo-Name forehead name tags. Simply peel off the adhesive backing, slap on the forehead and never be confused again!

NEED HELP SEEING AT NIGHT? Verona Opticians provide night lenses, telescopes, binoculars and free eye-tests. See perfectly from any balcony and never lose sight of your lover again!

SITUATIONS WANTED

POSITION REQ'D FOR FREE SPIRIT. I can fly, arrange masques, create food from nowhere and generally make myself useful around your archipelago. Contact Ariel on Mediterranean 0888976.

FREELANCE PSYCHOPATH FOR HIRE. Swordplay, invasions, bodyguard duties, etc. I am available following an unsuccessful attempt on public office. Call Coriolanus on Rome 776591

KINGDOM REQ'D. Experienced King now available for hire. Daughters have taken over family business. Employers must provide for large retinue.

LOOKING FOR FORTUNE TELLERS? Three experienced, old, extremely ugly crones available for short-term prophesying and cauldron stirring duties. Royalty preferred.

BOHEMIAN RHAPSODY

Leontes Accuses Polixenes Of Making Music With His Missus

King Leontes (25) of Sicilia has accused Polixenes (26), King of Bohemia, of committing adultery with the Queen (21).

In a remarkable outburst, the King accused the Bohemian monarch of being the real father of the baby Queen Hermione is expecting. Polixenes has fled Sicilia for his own country, aided by the courtier Camillo.

Guilt

"You see?" argued Leontes. "Polixenes ran away. A sure sign of guilt."

When asked if Leontes' order to have Polixenes assassinated didn't have something to do with his abrupt departure, the King replied, "He's guilty! His flight merely adds to their familiarity. No, you mark my words, she's an adulteress, a traitor and a right-royal slapper."

Leontes has been accused of being paranoid.

"Me?" he said. "Paranoid? I'm totally sane. I know, you see, because these voices have been telling me how level-headed I am."

Prison

Queen Hermione has been committed to prison. In a statement issued by her solicitor Paulina, she denied all charges and vowed to wait for the results of tests.

The King has sent away to the Oracle at Delphi for DNA tests, forensic evidence and some prophecies hidden inside Chinese crackers.

Babe Exiled

The baby girl born to Hermione in prison has been exiled by King Leontes.

"It's obviously not mine," he said, "I don't want it."

Although information is uncertain, it is thought that the girl has been taken by the courtier Antigonus to a distant land.

"We'll have the baby put up for adoption," said Leontes. *"Or possibly just left exposed on the side of a mountain. Whatever."*

SUSPICIOUS MINDS

EXCLUSIVE

Leontes' Suspicions Destroy His Family

Queen Hermione and Prince Mamilus are dead as a result of the turmoil in their family. The family has been split apart by Leontes' accusations of betrayal and adultery. The Prince took sick when his mother was accused and never recovered. The Queen died in seclusion, from a mystery disease.

"They died of broken hearts, pure and simple," said Paulina, the Queen's closest associate. "The King went mad, and his madness has destroyed his family."

Despite assurances from the Delphic oracle that his wife was not guilty, Leontes refused to believe in her innocence.

"What do they know about it?" he fumed. "A load of vestal virgins in togas sniffing incense and prognosticating. Call that a modern police force? Because I don't."

Deaths

Immediately the King scoffed at the pronouncement the news came that his son had died. The Queen collapsed and was taken from court, only to fall into a coma and die a few moments later.

"She just couldn't cope with the shock," said Paulina. "To look at her, you'd hardly think she was dead. But take it from me she is. No, really, I mean it."

Leontes has been shattered by the news, and has realized how wrong his accusations were.

"I don't know what got into me," he said. "I just couldn't control myself. Now I'll have to live with my actions for the rest of my life. I've lost my wife, my son and my daughter."

THE ORACLE HAS SPOKEN

Here is the official judgement from the Delphic Oracle, as read out at the trial of Hermione.

From the Office of Apollo To Whom It May Concern
Hermione is chaste; Polixenes blameless; Elvis dead; Camillo a true subject; Leontes a jealous tyrant; his innocent babe truly begotten; and the King shall live without an heir, if that which is lost be not found.
You have not been charged for this message.
Love and Kisses Apollo.
PS: Desdemona is innocent as well... oh no, hang on, that's a different story.

THERE'S A BEAR BEHIND!
Grizzly Stalks The Hills Of Bohemia
Unnamed Mariner Eaten Alive

The remains of a mariner have been discovered on a Bohemian hillside – yet another victim of the bear that has been causing terror in these parts.

"I saw the man trying to get back to his ship," said a passing shepherd, "which was quite difficult as Bohemia is landlocked. How he got here in the first place I don't know. He must have built up a lot of speed to get over the Alps."

Eaten

But the poor traveller never made it back aboard. Instead he was eaten by the bear.

"It was a terrible sight," said the shepherd. "This huge monster just grabbed him and tore him in half. I think his name was Antigonus – that was what he was shouting when the bear got him. Or he might have been called get-off-me-you-ugly-brute."

Baby

The sailor left behind an unusual package – a baby girl, in a basket. She has since been adopted by the shepherds.

"We're going to call her 'Don't-bite-me-there-you-monster' after the bloke who left her. Or possibly Perdita."

The unfortunate victim has been buried. "There wasn't much of him left, actually," said the shepherd. "We didn't bother using a coffin. We fitted it all in a shoebox."

SHEPHERD SPY
Prince Florizel Discovered Having Rumpy Pumpy In The Country

Prince Florizel has been escaping from the Palace and getting off with a shepherdess, according to a top secret government report.

The report, put together at the behest of King Polixenes, accuses the Prince of neglecting his duties and spending all his time with a simple country girl.

"This is unacceptable behaviour in a future King," warned his father. "This girl is obviously of a low social background. I mean, most of her friends are sheep. That's no background for a queen."

Love

Florizel is unrepentant.

"I love her," he said. "Not only is she a wonderful girl, she can shear a sheep in fifteen seconds. Whatever else, I'll never have to go to the barber's again."

Now the Prince intends to flee the country and travel to Sicilia.

"If we are not accepted here, we will go somewhere we are welcome," he said. "I'm getting on the first boat out of here."

IS STAT-YOU DARLING?

Hermione Returns As Living Statue

Bear Pardoned

It's a fairy-tale ending. Hermione has come back from the dead to be reunited with King Leontes.

The reunion took place when Leontes visited an exhibition to see a statue of his long-dead wife.

"I thought the carver had done a good piece of work," he said. "Not only was it very well sculpted, he'd even aged her. I mean, she had grey hair, stretch marks and everything."

Lesson

As the King looked at the statue, it descended from the plinth and embraced the King. It was, in fact, Queen Hermione. For sixteen years she had been biding her time to return.

"We wanted to teach the King a lesson," said Paulina, who planned the stunt. "We were just waiting for the right moment."

Perdita

The day was complete when the shepherdess who had arrived in Sicilia in the company of Prince Florizel was discovered to be the long-lost daughter of Hermione and Leontes.

"It's a real family reunion," said a close friend. "There were lots of tears and lots of laughter. In fact, the only thing that marred the day was that Cilla Black kept leaping out and yelling 'surprise' at the top of her voice."

To cap the general mood of festivities, the bear has been pardoned.

"*He was only acting naturally,*" said Prince Florizel. "*And, in a way, he's the most natural thing about this whole tale.*"

SENT OFF!

Richard Ends Grudge Match With Red Cards

The trial of combat between Bolingbroke and Mowbray ended in farce yesterday when King Richard II ordered both players off the field and into exile.

The fight was due to take place on St. Lambert's Day, in Coventry, at the National Expiration Centre.

"This was one of the worst refereeing decisions I have ever seen," fumed an angry Bolingbroke. "We hadn't even started fighting. So how we deserved sending off is beyond me."

Bolingbroke looks likely to be suspended for six years, whilst Mowbray faces a lifetime ban.

The fight was arranged to put to rest Bolingbroke's accusations that Mowbray was a murderer and traitor. Initially Richard agreed to the contest, even setting a time and date. But before the game had even kicked off, he banished both participants.

The news comes as a bitter blow to John of Gaunt, Bolingbroke's father and manager.

"The boy is gutted," he said. "He was looking forward to the chance to prove himself and now he's got to spend years overseas. I'm an old man, so I don't think he'll ever play for me again."

All this post-match comment has not amused the King.

"They had better watch it," he said. "Any more comments from John of Gaunt and I'll confiscate his land. I don't care if he is my uncle."

BOLING-BACK!

Bolingbroke Invades While Richard's In Ireland

Henry Bolingbroke has returned to England, only a few months after his banishment. This time, however, he is at the head of an invading army.

"He's taking the chance to invade while the King has nipped out to deal with the Irish rebellion," said a stressed-out Duke of York. "What's more, with loads of noblemen on Bolingbroke's side, it's not looking good."

Return

Meanwhile, Bolingbroke is insisting that all he wants is the return of his father's lands. After the death of his father, John of Gaunt, Richard confiscated all his wealth.

"When my dad died, the King unlawfully nicked all his possessions," he said. "All I want is my land back. Nothing more. Well, perhaps a bit more. We'll just have to wait and see."

Taxes

The King, meanwhile, faces a difficult task. Already unpopular with the people for heavy taxes, he has not yet returned from Ireland.

"If you ask me, Richard's picked a bad time to go abroad," said an unnamed Duke. "And no one knows where he's got to. It's been ages since anyone spotted Dick."

OLD ADAM'S GARDEN TIPS

Old Adam The Gardener Brings You Words Of Wisdom From The Compost Heap

Hello my old beauties,

It's that time of year when I can't wait to whip out my dibber and prod it into the earth. But for those of you who are wondering what to be getting on with next, here's a list of jobs that will need doing.

• Bind up your young dangling apricocks.

If they're too heavy, they will only cause problems for you later on in life. So make sure your twigs are well supported, and make sure your bodkin isn't too tight.

• Prune the fast growing sprays.

Anything too lofty must be cut down. That's true in gardens and it's true in life.

• Root out the weeds.

These nasty little blighters will do nothing but drain away the nourishment from the soil. Get rid of them, I say. Either burn them, or throw them into next door's garden.

• Wound the bark.

A judicious use of the knife will make the tree stronger in the long run.

• Execute the King.

Oops, how did that get in there?

Meanwhile, a correspondent writes:

Dear Adam,
Why should we keep our gardens in order when our sea-walled garden, the whole land, is full of weeds, choked with flowers and generally a right royal mess?
Yours,
Metaphorical of Wandsworth

Dear Metaphorical,
Well, it will all sort itself out in the long run. If you ask me we're safer sticking to gardening. It's less complicated.

And anyway, I hear the King is in the prison, so no doubt some pruning will shortly take place. My advice, keep your sickle sharp and your mangel-wurzels to yourself and you'll be all right.

Old Adam

If you're a fan of Old Adam's Garden Tips, you'll love this new book, from Parchment Paperbacks

Thoughts From My Compost Heap

by Old Adam the Gardener

Includes Adam's deepest thoughts on such subjects as

• When is the best time to plant rhubarb?
• What kinds of herbs are best to ward off nosey neighbours?
• Why is this sea-wall'd garden grown into such decay?
• How rude does a carrot have to look before you can charge people entry?
• Does "apricock" mean apricot, or is it merely a cheap double entendre?

Thoughts From My Compost Heap is available through all semi-literate flower-stalls and dung-heaps.

DICK'S DEAD!

Deposed King Killed In Castle Brawl

Bolingbroke is Henry IV Pt. One

BARD EXCLUSIVE

Where Is Bolingbroke Junior?

Meanwhile rumour and gossip abounds about the behaviour of Henry, son of Bolingbroke.

The young man, who will one day become King if Bolingbroke takes over, is reported to be out bingeing with friends.

"He's a great talent is the boy," said his father. "But he's too headstrong. He doesn't know how to control himself. Still, I expect it's just a phase he's going through."

Richard II (22), the deposed monarch, has been killed in his prison cell.

It appears that he refused to eat his food on the grounds that it was poisoned. He was then attacked and stabbed.

"He asked me to taste his food for him," said his gaoler. "But I was under instructions not to do that any more. I think he knew then that the game was up. He started attacking us and then some men burst in and that was that. Before we knew it, he was dead."

It seems likely that the King was to be poisoned, but forestalled the plan.

Bolingbroke

The murderer, Sir Piers Exton, claimed that he was acting on behalf of Bolingbroke.

"I thought that Henry wanted Richard out of the way. But he didn't seem very thankful. Honestly, some people have no gratitude."

In a brief press release, Henry Bolingbroke said that he regretted the incident.

"Whilst I may have wished him dead, I was never serious," he said. "Some people can't take a joke, apparently. I suppose I'll have to be King now."

New King

The new King will be known as Henry IV Part One.

"These are volatile times," said a member of the College of Heralds. "If he lives more than a few years he can be called Part Two, but most Kings don't make it past the first episode."

ROTTENHAM HOTSPUR

Headstrong Harry Is Preparing To Rebel

Harry Percy (23), nicknamed Hotspur, has defeated the rebellious Scots. But now he is refusing to hand over the prisoners to King Henry IV Part One.

"They're my prisoners to do with as I want," said the hot-headed Hotspur. "No one tells me what to do."

Furious

The King is reported to be furious.

"Everyone knows that you're supposed to hand over all prisoners to the King so that I can claim the ransom money," he said. "Not that I want it for myself, of course. It's just traditional, that's all."

The argument has escalated after the King refused to ransom Hotspur's brother-in-law Mortimer.

"The King won't have anything to do with Mortimer," said a source. "Mainly because Richard II declared that Mortimer was his natural successor as King. So Henry is quite happy for Mortimer to languish in jail. The last thing he wants is Mortimer swanning around, giving himself heirs."

Rebellion

The split has fuelled rumours that Hotspur is preparing to fight against the King.

"The Percy family helped the King depose Richard. But they've had nothing but ingratitude ever since," said a family friend. "I think young Hotspur's getting fed up with it."

Nickname

Some say Henry Percy was given the nickname Hotspur because of his high sense of honour, a subject on which he is touchy and hot tempered.

"I thought it was because he fights with a lot of flair but rarely actually wins the championship," said one commentator.

ONCE MORE UNTO THE BAR

"Prince Hazza In Bad Company" Claims Report

Prince Hal (21), or Hazza as he is known to his fans, is spending a fortune on drink and women.

That's the conclusion from a secret government report commissioned by his father, King Henry IV Part One.

And the report lays much of the blame on the Prince's companions, including the notorious Sir John "Five Bellies" Falstaff.

Robbery

There have even been claims that the Prince has been mixed up in highway robbery.

"No one's exactly sure what happened," said the sheriff investigating the case. "But someone answering Sir John's description – hugely fat, wheezing and drunk – was involved in robbing some travellers of three hundred marks. If it wasn't Sir John then the only other explanation is that there's a kleptomaniac hippo on the loose."

Rumours

Sir John, however, denies all.

"I was robbed myself," he argued. "Only I am not at liberty to tell you who the perpetrator is. No names, no pack drill, you know the form."

Amidst all these rumours, Hazza has promised to make good any damages and to repay any losses.

"He's completely irresponsible," said a palace spokesman. "He's such a talented soldier and Prince, but he's throwing it all away on booze. If only he'd get himself fit again, he could still fight for England."

"He's behaving like the P*** Artist Formerly Known As Prince"

THE WELSH ARE REVOLT-ING!

Prince In Palace Showdown

Hazza has been urged to mend his ways and come to his country's aid.

In a tense showdown, the King met with his wayward son and called on him to "pull himself together".

"They're not getting on too well at the moment," said a palace source. "The King thinks that Hazza should stop drinking, while the Prince reckons he can kick the habit any time he likes."

Rebellion

The conference comes as the Welsh under Owen Glendower are allied with the Scots and Harry Hotspur's men in a rebellion against the King.

"This is an important moment for young Hazza," said an observer. "His international future is on the line.

"*I just hope he can rise to the occasion.*"

The Big Front

The War Reports of Sir John Falstaff

As the country prepares for war, we are honoured to bring you this exclusive extract from the new book *For King And Country – The War Diaries of Sir John Falstaff*

Sir John is leading a crack regiment – The King's Own Alcoholic Division - into battle at Shrewsbury. Here, he gives us a unique insight into the life of a modern war machine.

Dec 1st – War is declared. At first I believed I would be declared unfit for action, on account of the fact that I am hugely overweight, heavily hung-over and suffering from an old war-wound which I don;t like to talk about. (It's a clinical condition. I've got a note from my doctor.) I thought it my duty to point this out to the Prince, but he would have none of it.

"Your country needs you Sir John," he said to me. "We can't win this thing without you."

What could I do? Odds, I love that boy!

Dec 5th – I have been trailing through the country recruiting. I have tried to recruit young, well-off men, you know, yeoman's sons, rich bachelors about to get married. But they insisted on buying themselves out of their obligations. So what could I do? I took the money and got left with this load of Dad's Army rejects. War is an ugly thing. Give me drinking any day. Ah me, I wish it were bed time and all well.

Dec 7th – The eve of the war. I have met with the Prince who swore to protect me. As if I needed it, for I am a lion. Have spent some of the day scouting the location, seeking out the best places to hide. Not for myself, you understand, but in order that I might flush out any of the enemy who try hiding.

Dec 8th – The battle began early. After killing about twenty men (I lost count) I emerged from my strategic viewpoint in the bushes to find Sir Walter Blunt slain. He had disguised himself as the King and been killed by Douglas of Scotland. A few minutes later the same Douglas attacked me. Suddenly overcome with remorse and a hatred of killing, I cunningly pretended to be dead in order to save him from punishment.

Meanwhile the Prince defeated Hotspur in straight combat. But unknown to Hal, he hadn't quite finished the job. So although Hal had stabbed him through the heart, I had to fight him and finish Hotspur off. So, you see, it was really me who killed the rebel leader. Still, I don't like to boast. Nor do I expect high reward.

An earldom will do me fine.

SOMETHING OLD, SOMETHING NEW, SOMETHING BORROWED...

Love-cheat Gets A Further Fortune From His Female

Sir John Falstaff, the one-time hero of Shrewsbury, escaped arrest yesterday for debt by borrowing even more!

The rotund rascal, famous for his girth and notorious for his friendship with Hazza, was hauled up before the Chief Justice. He was accused of breaking his promise to marry Mistress Quickly and failing to repay money he borrowed from her.

Misunderstanding

"It's all a terrible misunderstanding," said Sir John. "Unfortunately the woman is completely mad. It makes me almost embarrassed to borrow money from her."

Sir John was initially arrested by two officers. Then, after a meeting with Mistress Quickly, all charges were dropped.

. "He explained the situation to me and I promised to lend him ten pounds and give him a meal," said the hostess. "I'm not quite sure why I agreed to do that, but he made it seem so plausible at the time."

IT'S THE SALVA-TION ARMY!

Rebel Army Regroups Under Archbishop

The rebel army, although defeated at Shrewsbury, has regrouped. And the Archbishop of York is its new leader.

They hope to benefit from the rumours of French aggression towards King Henry, as well as the tide of public opinion which has clearly swung against the monarch.

"People have not forgotten what he did to Richard," said the Archbishop. "The Bible says you should forgive your enemies and I intend to anoint King Henry. With a large sword."

And In Part Two...

The College of Heralds have declared that Henry is now officially King Henry IV Part Two.

"He survived this far," they said. "Although we hear he's ill. So I doubt he'll make it to the third stage."

King Henry's illness is, according to his doctors, stress related.

"He has so much responsibility that he's not sleeping properly," said his physician. "He's not getting any younger and he's also worried about his son. The Prince hasn't even sent him a get well card."

YOU'RE NICKED, FATHER!

Archbishop Of York And Rebel Leaders Duped

The rebellion is over. It was ended by a spectacular piece of trickery by Prince John of Lancaster, younger son of King Henry IV Part Two.

He told the rebel leaders that if they lay down their arms their grievances would be addressed," said Westmoreland. "Unfortunately they took that to mean that they would be pardoned. But he never said that."

The Archbishop was typically Christian in defeat.

"Prince John is a cheat and a liar," he said. "He is the lowest form of traitorous vermin. Bless him."

Evil

John of Lancaster was unrepentant.

"Rebellion is an evil act," he told us. "Especially for a Vicar. My father has the divine right of Kings. The Archbishop should have stuck to preaching."

Others, however, viewed the whole affair with cynicism.

"Henry didn't get the throne through divine right, but through having Richard killed," said a source, who did not wish to be named. "I don't know what God thinks of all this, but I don't suppose he's happy with either side."

Is Hazza Fit To Be King?

With King Henry running out of parts, the crown will pass to young Hazza. But is this hard-drinking, womanizing, party-going man mature enough to be King?

As the King lies dying, the debate rages on in the palace – has young Prince Hal got what it takes to rule the nation?

Brothers

His brothers, like the Dukes of Gloucester and Clarence, are on record as saying he cannot reform.

The Earl of Warwick, however, thinks that Hal can turn himself around and resurrect his career.

"I think he's just been spending time studying people," he said. "After all, the majority of citizens in the island are lying, cheating drunkards. It's one of England's defining characteristics. If you want to govern them you have to understand them. I think he'll be back, and better than ever."

Drink

"He's a grand lad," said his long-time friend Sir John "Five Bellies" Falstaff. "Certainly a great deal better than his younger brother John. I tell you that man has no sense of humour because he doesn't drink."

Indeed, Sir John is the only one who believes that drinking has actually benefited Prince Hal.

"He's naturally cold blooded, like his father," he said. "But after a few pints of sherry he's a different man; warm blooded, hot and valiant. If you ask me he doesn't drink enough. But then, none of us do."

SO LONG HAZZA HELLO HENRY

Prince Reforms To Take On The Top Job

King Henry V was crowned today in Westminster Abbey, and vowed to live a reformed life.

"I've done some bad things, I know," he said. "But I always knew that I'd reform. I knew that one day I would achieve my destiny. Presume not I am the thing I once was. I'm totally changed."

He was reconciled with his late father before the King died. The King even advised the Prince how to bring the country together and restore his sullied reputation. "I intend to unite the country behind me in the time-honoured way – by killing a lot of foreigners. It's always worked before."

"Let me get this right," said an onlooker. "We're going to go to war with France to stop the Lords from quarrelling and to improve Henry's image? And he's supposed to be a good king?"

Rebuff

The new King showed his true colours by ruthlessly dismissing his former associates. Sir John Falstaff was brutally rebuffed when he approached the new King, despite their long friendship.

"Sir John called out to the lad, but the Prince claimed not to know him. More than that he virtually handed him over to the Chief Justice for arrest."

Sir John was taken to the Fleet prison. The staff of the Boar's Head, where Prince Hal spent so much of his time, were also arrested, with Mistress Quickly and Doll Tearsheet taken into custody.

Sir John, however, was putting a brave face on things.

"I am sure he means to meet with me secretly," he said.

"He would never send me away, would he? Not his old friend Jack. Not sweet Jack, kind Jack, true Jack. He wouldn't do that, surely?"

AND BALLS TO YOU, JACQUES!

French Ambassador Delivers Tennis Balls In 'Tribute'

Henry Declares War

Henry V has declared war on France after an insulting exchange with the French Ambassador.

The Ambassador told Henry that the French King thought he should stay at home and play games. He then gave the King a box of tennis balls.

"The King was furious," said a palace spokesman. "I mean he doesn't even play tennis. Now if they had been dominos or darts, that might have been different."

Justified

Earlier the King had heard from the Archbishop of Canterbury that the war was certainly justified.

"The Archbishop delivered a long lecture on the principle of female succession and its justification in the Bible. To cut a long speech short, he said that God was on our side."

Others, however, were less sure of themselves.

"For one thing, Henry needs a foreign war to improve his position in the polls," said Henry Scroop, a vowed opponent of the King. "And as for the Archbishop – well, given that Parliament is threatening to take away half the possessions of the Church, it's hardly surprising that he's trying to get into Henry's good books, is it?"

The Archbishop argued his case. "War is justifiable under certain circumstances," he said. "If you are fighting a great moral evil, if the church is threatened, or if the enemy eats garlic, wears stripey jumpers and speaks with a funny accent. It's all in the Bible. Probably."

Death of a Legend

Sir John Dies of A Fever

Legendary drinker and scoundrel Sir John Falstaff is dead.

He died of a fever yesterday at his lodgings in an ale house. His faithful friend Mistress Quickly was with him at the end, along with some other of his associates who were preparing to go to France.

"He was a great man," said Mistress Quickly. "Maybe not in the conventional way, but he had a great heart. And physically, of course, he was enormous."

Decline

The death certificate recorded the cause of the knight's death as "a quotidian ague". But sources say that he had been in decline ever since his beloved Prince Hal ascended to the throne.

"It wasn't the fever that did for him," said Mistress Quickly. "The King killed his heart, if you ask me."

Sir John will be remembered for his ability to drink like a fish. An alcoholic fish. A depressed alcoholic fish.

But he was more than a drinker. "He was kind, roguish, cowardly, and deceitful," said Mistress Quickly. "He missed his calling. He should have been a politician."

Dame Alice's Guide to French

For all those of our readers thinking of visiting France, either to stock up on duty free or to kill lots of Frenchmen in a brutal and psychopathic way, here's Dame Alice, a gentlewoman of Queen Katherine, to translate a few phrases.
Armed with these handy phrases, and a big sword, you'll find your stay in France relaxing and profitable.

La main, Les doigts, Le coude
The hand, the fingers, the elbow

Le plume de ma tante
My aunt is covered with feathers

Chacun a son gout
Please don't kill me, brave Englishman

Chambourcy nouvelle
Yes, of course you can have my castle

Est-il impossible d'échapper la force de ton bras?
It is possible that chaps in the forces wear brassieres?

O prenez miséricorde! Ayez pitie de moi!
Take my miserable corduroy trousers. Have pity on me!

Rue de la gare
I surrender

Charles Aznavour, Sacha Distel
Please do not torture me

Moi aussi
I am an Australian

Vin de pays?
Do you wish to purchase my lorry?

Coq au vin?
Does your chicken wish to purchase my lorry?

Du vin, du pain, du Boursin
I'll even throw in some free cheese.

Sauf votre honneur, le français que vous parlez, il est meilleur que l'anglais lequel je parle.
Kiss me, you strangely-haircutted hunk of English Henry-hood.

Cry Gotcha for Harry, England and St George!
Henry takes Honfleur

English forces have captured the city of Honfleur in the opening salvo of the war with the French.

The Governor of the town surrendered when it became clear that the Dauphin was not going to send reinforcements.

"I rang the Dauphin," said the Governor, "but he told me they weren't quite ready. I think the English attacked sooner than they thought. They must have caught an earlier ferry or something."

Unimpressed

King Henry led the troops into victory with a shout of "Cry God for Harry, England and St George." Some troops, however, were not impressed.

"Never mind all this shouting about St George," said one soldier. "I wish I was back in the George alehouse in London.

"I would give all my fame for a pot of ale and safety."

A JUST WAR?

Do you think the war against France is justified? Or are you opposed to all forms of aggression?

We asked you, the public, for your honest opinion.

As a leading cannonball maker I believe that this war is totally justified. In fact, I think we should have a war every year, just to keep our spirits up.
William G.

If the cause be not good, then the King himself has a heavy reckoning to make when all those legs and arms and heads chopped off in the cause of battle shall join together at the last day.
Michael W. (Private)

Of course it's justified. I'm the K... I mean he's the King after all.
Harry Le Roy (Welsh Fusiliers, apparently)

I think the war is totally justified. Partly because those lands were owned by Edward III several centuries ago so should still be ours, but mainly because I get to own a load of nice new cathedrals.
Archbishop of C.

I've never trusted him since the day he stopped buying a round.
Bardolph

Have your say.

Is the King right? Or is he a semi-fascist dictator with a personality disorder?
Tell us what you think in our exciting phone poll.
Dial 01 for 'I think the King is doing a great job.'
Dial 02 for 'I think the King is a pompous warmonger with a terrible haircut.'

FRENCH FRIED CRISP'N' DIE

Crispin Day Massacre Of French Forces

"We're Like One Big Happy Family," Says King

"We few, we happy few, we band of brothers, we three kings, we are the champions!"

Those were the words of a jubilant King Henry in the aftermath of an astonishing victory at Agincourt. The English army beat the French who outnumbered them five to one.

"It's a victory for our superior courage, superior nerve and superior strength," said one commander. "That plus the fact we have these flipping great longbows and they don't."

Jubilant

The King was in jubilant mood.

"We lost hardly any men," he said. "Just Edward Duke of York, Earl of Suffolk, Sir Richard Keighley, Davy Gam and a few other commoners that nobody bothers much about."

Now the King is intent on securing a lasting peace with France and possibly getting his hands on the daughter of the King.

"They have offered me the hand of their daughter in marriage," said the King, "with the rest of her phased in by 1420."

BRING BACK WORK FOR WELFARE
"Give Us Ten Thousand More" Says Duke

On the eve of the battle a leading nobleman called for national conscription of all the unemployed.

"If we had but one ten thousand of all those in England who do no work today!" exclaimed the Duke of Westmorland. "Then we'd have... er... ten thousand more men than we do at the moment. And that's a fact."

The King, however, has dismissed the scheme.

"Apart from the obvious fact that we are due to fight in a few hours' time and they're still in their beds, I believe that the fewer men the greater share of honour."

Thief Hanged

Bardolph, a petty thief in the army, has been hanged for pilfering and theft.

A former associate of Prince Hal, he is yet another old acquaintance to be abandoned by the Prince. The news comes in the wake of Sir John Falstaff's funeral and the death of Doll Tearsheet, ex cabaret dancer, from a sexually transmitted disease.

"The King could have saved his old friend but he didn't," said one source. "He may appear a saint, but there's a dark side to him, if you ask me."

Atrocities Reported

In the retreat from Agincourt the French destroyed the British camp. They killed the boys who served there and burned the tents.

"This was totally against the code of war," said an observer. "Everyone knows you don't attack defenceless serving lads. We would never do a thing like that."

In a retaliatory gesture, King Henry ordered that all French prisoners should have their throats cut.

"Fair's fair," he said.

THERE'S A NEW KID IN TOWN
Henry V Dies Leaving Boy Prince In Charge

Henry V, hero of Agincourt, scourge of the French, leader of the nation, father of the bride and sign of the times is dead.

He died yesterday, leaving his heir, Henry VI Part One, as king. Already constitutional experts are predicting a long reign.

"We're very excited," said one. "We think this lad has it in him to go as far as part three, maybe even part four, who knows? After all, he's only a child now, so there has to be hope for a lot of sequels."

Omens

Others, however, are less hopeful.

"The omens are not good," said Lord Gloucester, the Lord Protector. "There is bad news from France, but when I asked the King if he wanted me to get some soldiers, he just dribbled. I know he's only nine months old, but I expect a bit more leadership than that. The only soldiers he likes are the ones he has with egg for his tea."

"This is a recipe for disaster," said one court correspondent. "Henry's death has left a power vacuum. And every time you get a vacuum, you know that somebody is going to clean up."

LAWS OF THE ROSES

A legal argument between a group of students was decided by plucking different coloured roses.

The argument, between Richard Plantagenet and the Earl of Somerset, led to heated exchanges in the students' union. Eventually the arguing sides moved into the garden, where they took a vote.

"We decided that each student would pick different coloured roses," said a student. "If you agreed with Richard, you chose a white rose. If you supported Somerset, you chose a red rose. It seemed like a good idea at the time."

Argument

"It didn't really solve anything," said a witness. "It just turned into a sort of family feud between the York clan and Somerset, who is descended from the Duke of Lancaster.

"Still, I daresay it will all blow over.

"*After all, it's nothing to have a war about, is it?*"

Defeat In France

The English army has been badly beaten in France. Early news indicates that we have lost Paris, Poitiers, Rheims, Rouen and Milton Keynes. Not to mention Guernsey.

We have also lost Champagne.

"I don't know what we're going to do for Christmas," said the Duke of Bedford, who is protector of France. "I'll have to use Asti Spumante instead."

MAID IN FRANCE

Joan "La Pucelle" Defeats The Dauphin

The French have a new secret weapon. Her name: Joan La Pucelle, or Joan the Maid.

After being visited by a vision of Mary, she now leads the French armies.

"She's incredible," said our French correspondent. "She defeated the Dauphin in single combat as a proof of her supernatural powers. She can predict the future, lead an army, and uncover hidden identities. Not only that, but she makes a mean quiche lorraine."

"She's amazing," said the Dauphin. "The only thing she can't do is marry. Apparently she has sworn a vow of celibacy. Which is just as well, because let's face it, she's a frightening woman."

La Pucelle – latest news

The forces of France have captured two cities and then lost them both.

They recaptured Orleans, only to be thrown out by Lord Talbot a few hours later. Now the process has been repeated at Rouen, where Joan took the city and then lost it again.

"It's getting very confusing," said a source. "It's like a game of Monopoly out there."

Hundred Years War – Latest Scores

York (1) **2**	**Lancaster**(1) **2**	**Rome** (0) **6**	**Carthage** (6) **6**
Richard 22, 54	Winchester,	Caesar 46	Pompey 5
	Bishop of 33, 82	Caesim 49	Pompous 8, 42
		Caesit 54	Pompand-circum
Joan of Arc (3) **5**	**Talbot** (4) **4**	Cassius 78	stance14, 27, 35
Arc, J. (Miss) 19	Talbot (Snr) 3,	Bigredbus 86	
Jourdain, 24, 35	5, 8	Toysarus 88	
Anjou, Margaret of	Talbot (Jnr) 21		
56, 68		**Venice** (3) **4**	**Turkey** (0) **0**
(Arc sent off for failing a Witch Test)		Othello 14	
		Iago 17	
Burgundy(4) **5**	**Chablis** (3) **4**	Sago 19	
Chatillon 14, 15	Hanun 23, 26, 34	Awayougo 55	
Alençon 17	Shearer 67		
Hatandcoaton 19		**Montagues** (0) **3**	**Capulets** (3) **3**
Onandon 55		Romeo 18	Barnes 23, 24, 28
		Benvolio 20	
Scotland (3) **3**	**Norway** (0) **0**	Toworkwego 29	
Macbeth 20			
MacJock 28		**Greeks** (2) **4**	**Trojans** (1) **5**
BigMac 36		Ajax 12, 48	Hector 15, 60
		Dettol 14	Troilus 46
		Flash 54	Helen 75, 80

STONE ME!

Hooligans throw stones during Parliament

The latest measures to control hooliganism on the terraces failed today when supporters of rival teams threw stones at one another.

The Gloucester and Winchester fans engaged in pitched battle through London's streets, as Parliament met to try to solve the problem.

"All supporters were banned from bringing weapons into the ground," said the Mayor of London, whose forces came under attack. "So they just picked up stones and started chucking them at each other."

The dispute started when Gloucester, the Lord Protector, accused the Bishop of Winchester of laying an ambush for him.

"He's jealous of my power and position," said Richard of Gloucester. "As the King's uncle I have been appointed Protector. The sad thing is I have to protect the King from people like the Bishop."

Inside the Parliament, young King Henry managed to secure a fragile truce between the two enemies. He also conferred the title Duke of York onto Richard Plantagenet and decided to cross the seas.

"It is our will to be crowned King in France," said Henry. "Besides, I really want to go to EuroDisney."

FLOWER POWER

Henry Intervenes in rose wars

The so called 'war of the roses' has drawn the attention of the young King, who has tried to defuse the situation.

The two factions – followers of the Dukes of York and Somerset – have been arguing for months now. The latest spat involved an argument between two followers on the boat across the Channel.

"I think they'd had too much duty free," said one observer. "They're still arguing about that point of law."

Sides

Henry chose a red rose, but claimed that all he was doing was picking a buttonhole.

"It's all very well for him to play the innocent," said the Duke of York. "But everyone knows that the red rose is the symbol of New Lancaster. I don't think the King should be taking sides, even if he was just trying to make a point."

Escalation

"I don't think the King really understands what is going on here," said Exeter. "This is more than a petty dispute. It has its origins in the way Henry's grandfather had Richard, Duke of Cambridge, executed for treason. His supporters on the Lancaster side have never forgotten that. Pretending it's just a flower won't make the problem go away."

TALBOT BETRAYED

"Rose" squabble leads to Talbot defeat

Lord Talbot, for so long England's only real warrior in France, is dead. His men were cut off and left unsupported after a squabble between the Dukes of York and Somerset left him without reinforcements.

"Somerset was supposed to provide York with horsemen to relieve Lord Talbot," said a spokesman for the Yorkists. "But they never turned up. It's all Somerset's fault."

Ill-Judged

Somerset, meanwhile, was blaming the other forces.

"This was an ill-judged, badly planned expedition," said Lord Somerset. "It was obviously planned so that Talbot would die and York could seize power. York set him on; York should have sent him aid."

While the two sides squabbled, Talbot's forces were overwhelmed.

"Talbot was betrayed by a pair of squabbling schoolgirls," said Sir William Lucy. "The fraud of England trapped him, not the force of France."

JOAN ALONE La Pucelle is Captured and Sentenced to Death

Joan La Pucelle, the witch who has been leading France has been captured and tried by the war crimes tribunal.

They found her guilty on three counts: being a witch; wearing trousers; and being offensively and gratuitously French.

At her trial Joan claimed that she could not be burnt at the stake as she was pregnant. When pressed, she claimed that the father was either the Dauphin, the Duke of Alençon or Reignier,

King of Naples.

"I think it was the panic talking," said one observer. "Her powers seem to have left her and she has been abandoned by her former allies. She is getting delusional now."

HARRY WILL MARRY

King weds his French Princess

King Henry is to marry Margaret of Anjou, daughter of the King of Naples, it was revealed today.

Margaret was brought to England by Lord Suffolk, following her capture during a siege.

"She's a lovely girl," said Lord Suffolk. "I'd marry her myself, if the King hadn't got there first."

Negotiations

The King will marry next May, after negotiations with the French have concluded. He will give her father the territories of Anjou and Maine as part of the deal.

"I don't think of it as losing a daughter," said her father, "as much as gaining a lot of territory."

Discontent

Some people do not approve of the match.

"She's not as sweet as she seems," said an Earl. "I think we're going to have trouble with her later."

PEACE WITH HONOUR?

The wars in France have been ended for now – with a peace treaty.

The King has decided that enough is enough. He has given in to general European pressure to sign a peace agreement.

Unwelcome

It has not been welcomed in all quarters, however.

"I can't believe that we worked so hard for this," said the Duke of York. "So many captains, gentlemen and soldiers have died. And for what? An effeminate peace. If you ask me, this can only lead to the loss of all France."

Rest

Others are more optimistic.

"Look, everyone needs a rest," said Warwick. "This peace treaty gives the French very little. But gives the rest of us a break. After all, we've been fighting the French since the beginning of Henry the Fifth's reign. It's getting a bit tedious now."

UNHAPPY MEDIUM

Duchess arrested, accused of sorcery

The Duchess of Gloucester has been arrested and accused of sorcery.

"She was part of a group of people detained during a raid," said a police spokesman. "From what we can gather they appear to have been conjuring up spirits."

The Duchess is reputed to have employed a disgraced priest, John Hume, as well as a witch, Margery Jourdain.

"I prefer to think of myself as a psychic consultant," said Margery from her cell yesterday. " 'Witch' is so passé, don't you think?"

Future

The purpose of their coven is uncertain.

"They appear to have been asking questions about the future," said the police spokesman. "You know, 'What shall become of the King?', 'What fate awaits Lord Suffolk?', 'Who is going to win the 3.30 at Kempton Park?' That sort of thing."

Punishment

The Duchess has already received her punishment.

"It's worse than we thought," said a family friend. "We were expecting her to be burnt at the stake, but she's actually been banished to the Isle of Man. A sort of living death really. I mean, you can't go out of your front gate without being run over by a motorcycle."

Enemies

In the wake of the decision, Humphrey, Duke of Gloucester has resigned as Lord Protector.

"He really loves his wife," said a friend. "Even if she is a witch."

The Duke has made many enemies, especially the Bishop of Winchester, Cardinal Beaufort. Indeed, it is rumoured that some of his opponents were behind the arrest of his wife.

Set-Up

"I'm sure this is a set up," said one witness. "There are these tiny clues. Like the fact that someone put up big signs saying 'coven this way' in the street outside."

TROUBLE GLOUCESTER!
Humphrey Murdered
Cardinal and Suffolk Accused

Duke Humphrey has been brutally assassinated. Police are still investigating, but there have already been claims that he was murdered at the express command of his enemies Cardinal Beaufort and the Duke of Suffolk.

"We are still investigating the motive," said the Chief Inspector. "He was the second most powerful man in England and whoever took over from him would effectively control the throne. So we're not stuck for suspects."

Charges

The Duke was already under investigation following charges of corruption and accessory to murder – charges he vehemently denied.

"This is the result of a huge power struggle that is going on around the King," said one observer. "If you ask me, his wife, Margaret, is not the virtuous young lady she would have us believe."

There are even rumours that the Queen is more friendly than she should be with Suffolk.

"She goes to visit Suffolk an awful lot," said a government source. "I'm sure it's not just for the bird watching."

Divine Retribution
Suffolk Killed, Cardinal Dead

The Duke of Suffolk has been killed by pirates, it was revealed yesterday.

He was on his way to exile in France, following his banishment by King Henry, when his ship was waylaid by buccaneers and he was killed.

Illness

Meanwhile, his confederate, Cardinal Beaufort, was suddenly struck down with a mystery illness.

"It was like he could see Duke Humphrey there the whole time," said his servant. "He was seeing a ghost.

"He kept shouting, 'Don't come near me!' and 'I didn't do it!' and 'Maybe I did do it, but I was only joking!'

"*I think he may have been suffering from a guilty conscience.*"

ANARCHY IN THE UK!
Rebels On The March

An army of rebels from Kent are marching on London, intent on seizing power for themselves. Their leader is Jack Cade. And he's claiming he is a descendant of the Duke of Clarence, third son of Edward III.

"It came as a big surprise to us," said a former colleague from the building company where Cade worked. "We thought his father was a shepherd and his mother a lace-maker. But apparently he was stolen from the cradle at birth and brought up in Kent. It just goes to show you can never tell."

Manipulated

There have been claims that the rebellion has been inspired by the Duke of York to unsettle the Kingdom. But Cade denies that he is being manipulated.

"We have a comprehensive list of demands," he said. "Cheaper bread, more hoops around our pots and better beer. All goods shall be held in common and we're going to kill all the lawyers."

Sir Humphrey Stafford has been sent with a force to intercept the rebellion.

"It's ridiculous," he said. "Their demands are ludicrous and immoral. Apart from that one about the lawyers – I quite like that one."

Peasants

Sir Humphrey is confident that the rebellion will be quickly dealt with.

"They're just a load of peasants," he said. "We'll send them back to Kent before they know what's happened to them."

BUTCHERY ON BLACKHEATH

The rebel force under Jack Cade have soundly defeated the government troops sent to sort them out. Sir Humphrey Stafford, the opposing general, was killed and the rest of his troops fled in panic.

Butcher

One rebel – Dick, a butcher from Ashford – was particularly heroic.

"He treated them like they were a side of lamb, or a lump of beef," said Cade. "Not only did he chop them into mincemeat, but several of them he also plucked and one he even stuffed with sage and onion."

The rebels have since taken Southwark, London Bridge and attacked the Tower of London.

Common

"I really want Park Lane, because then I can start building hotels," said Cade. "But from now on everyone must refer to me as Lord Mortimer, in honour of my heritage.

"And all things will be in common."

OH, THE CROWNED OLD DUKE OF YORK

York Claims Crown as Rebels Collapse

As one rebellion ends, another begins.

Jack Cade's peasants have collapsed in disarray. Their leader has fled in panic. But as their rebellion was defeated news has come that the Duke of York is in London, intent on claiming the crown.

York's invasion is the culmination of the so called "war of the roses", the dispute between the houses of York and Lancaster for control of the country.

"All I wanted was to see the Somerset influence removed," said the Duke of York. "All that scrumpy and clotted cream is no good for the country. However, when it became clear that the King was not going to have Somerset arrested, I decided to take over the country myself."

Disaster

"This is a disaster for the country," said an observer. "It now looks as though York was planning all along to challenge the monarchy. He arranged for Cade's rebellion to give him an excuse to bring troops into the country. And since then he's been marching them up and down hills like nobody's business."

Halfway

Military analysts claim that the result of the civil war will be hard to predict.

"It should go to York," said one, "especially as he's supported by Warwick. But he's only halfway there at the moment. He's neither up nor down."

ROTTEN TO THE CORE
Jack Cade killed in Orchard

Rebel leader Jack Cade has been killed hiding in an orchard in Kent.

He climbed into the orchard to scavenge for food, following a humiliating retreat from London. When the owner of the orchard, Sir Alexander Iden, challenged him, they fought and Cade was killed.

"I noticed him when someone grabbed one of my Pippins," said Iden. "He attacked me, but he was too feeble to fight properly."

Cade's body was thrown on a dunghill and his head taken to King Henry.

"He was a rotten apple, that one," said Sir Alexander. "I'm glad I had the chance to prune him."

BARD SPORTS

**All the Action
All the Time**

FIRST BLOOD TO YORKSHIRE

The first Roses match has been won by the Yorkshire team, playing against King Henry's First XI.

The match was played at St Albans and the Royalists were soon reduced to rubble by vicious fast bowling from Warwick and Salisbury.

Warwick felled Clifford of Cumberland with a brutal bouncer, while Somerset was forced to retire from the field due to being dead.

"We played well," said the Duke of York. "We bowled with hostility and batted with a straight bat. Now we're looking forward to the next match which will be in London. At Lord's, of course."

King Henry did not attend the post-match press conference, preferring instead to flee to London.

Yorkists
York (c) lbw Exeter 42
Warwick c & b Margaret . . .13
Salisbury b Margeret 26
Gloucester, R. hbw* Exeter .45
Pembroke run out 21
Stafford c Exeter b Somerset . .12
Faulconbridge run out 14
Eebagum not out 21
Ilkley Moor . . . .
Bartat . . . .
Trueman, F. . . . .
Total . . . . .194-7 declared

* Hump before wicket

Royalists
Henry, King (c) run out 25
Clifford (Sr) ret. hurt 9
Clifford (Jr) lbw Warwick . . .10
Somerset ret. dead 5
Buckingham c & b Salisbury .18
Margaret, Queen not out 99
Exeter b Bartat 3
Northumberland b Warwick . . .5
Westmorland b Salisbury 2
Legoland closed 15
Ampersand stabbed Gloucester .2
Total 193

**Whose side are you on?
Write to us and let us know which faction you support.
Write to The Bard, ~~Lancashire, no Yorkshire, no Lancashire~~, on the borders,
Bray, No Particular County At All.**

OVER MY DEAD BODY!

Henry Agrees York Can Be Next King

The Duke of York will be the next King, but he'll have to wait until King Henry is dead!

The agreement was hammered out in a packed Parliament.

"We have a peace deal worked out," said a spokesman. "Henry is to reign for his lifetime, but after that the throne will revert to Richard, Duke of York."

The deal effectively disinherits Henry's son, Prince Edward.

"I feel very let down," said the Prince. "I was looking forward to my coronation. I've even had the invitations printed and everything."

Appalling

Henry's wife, Margaret was equally dismissive.

"This is an appalling situation," she said. "I didn't put up with Henry for all these years to see the succession given away so easily. He didn't even put up a fight."

Army

Margaret is now planning to lead the army herself.

"If you want a job doing, you'd be better off doing it yourself," she said.

IRON LADY

Duke of York Killed By Queen Margaret

Queen Margaret's army swept through Wakefield yesterday, destroying the small Yorkist force that was there and capturing the Duke of York.

"We were simply outnumbered," said a soldier. "We had no choice."

The Queen herself joined the battle, leaving her husband at home.

"I tell you, she's a frightening woman," said one onlooker. "She wields that handbag like a broadsword. She killed Rutland, the Duke's son and then did for the Duke himself."

Paper Crown

Once the Duke was captured Margaret stood him on a molehill and made him wear a paper crown.

"It was a bit like Christmas," said a spectator. "Only then she stabbed him to death, which didn't seem much like the season of goodwill."

Gates

The Duke's head has been stuck on a pole above the gates to the city of York.

"It's quite attractive in a gory sort of way," said a visitor. "Although I'm not sure about the apple in the mouth."

WHAT'S ON...
Your Guide to the Best TV

8.00 Good Morning Troops!
With Henry V
The early morning programme that really brings you to the breach again!
Let other men of England lie in their beds while you get up and about with the monarch who really knows how to put you through your paces!

10.00 The Morning Service
This morning's service comes from Westminster Abbey, where Henry VI will meditate on the stresses and strains of life and the search for peace.

12.55 Today's Omens
A look at the meaning of today's weather with Margaret of Anjou. Will floods sink your fleets? Will there be three suns in the sky? Will the winter of your discontent be made glorious summer?

1.00 The News
Followed by **Local News** from Gloucester, Lancashire, Suffolk, Norfolk or whichever feudal system you happen to be under at the time.

1.30 Coronation Road
Another episode of this exciting new soap about next door neighbours who each want to get their hands on the crown. Today Richard poisons Henry's dog, whilst Edward plays with his rosary.

2.00 How Does She Do That?
Another look at the life of Joan of Arc, this time asking how she combined a career besieging Orleans and still had time to clean the bathroom.

3.00 Blue Pistol
Children's Magazine. This week Falstaff's sidekick shows you how to pick pockets and how to create an ale tankard out of the bottom of a washing-up liquid bottle.

3.30 Grandstand
Live coverage of the jousting from The Field of the Cloth of Gold. Plus full highlights of the siege of Honfleur.

6.00 Neville's Palace Party
See Preview

7.00 The Antiques Show
Discoveries include an original copy of the Magna Carta, Richard II's doublet and the teddy bear of Edward VI.

7.30 Eurovision Ballad Contest
England's Blondin is up against stiff competition from the French and Italian balladeers. Can his new song 'How Much Is That Monarchy In The Window?' carry away the top prize?

9.00 A Party Political Broadcast On Behalf of King Richard III
Or possibly on behalf of Henry VII. Or even Edward IV. It's a bit confusing at the moment.

9.30 One Foot in the Tomb
Another hilarious peek into the world of Harry Hotspur. This week his prisoners refuse to be ransomed and his wife starts to work for Margaret of Anjou.

10.00 Questing Time
Debate among several nobles about whether they should go on a Crusade or not.

Preview
Neville's Palace Party
Join Warwick the Kingmaker for another wacky, fun-filled castle adventure. This week contestants get the chance to compete for the ultimate prize.
Will Richard of Gloucester grab the crown or will he be gunged? See Jack Cade ambushed in the hilarious gotcha. And is Harry Richmond ready to 'run the risk'?

SHEPHERD'S PIE

I'd rather be a shepherd, says King

Henry has spoken at length about his sadness at the present civil war.

In an exclusive interview for the BBC (Burgundy Broadcasting Corporation) he talks of giving it all up to be a shepherd.

"I don't want to be a military leader," he said. "I want to be the King of people's hearts."

"It's pie in the sky, of course," said an observer. "He was destined to be King. Unfortunately he was also destined to be a bit of a prat."

The King speaks movingly of witnessing first-hand the division that civil war brings.

"I saw a son who had killed his father, and a father who had killed his son. That's what civil war does. Father against son. Brother against brother. Sister's mother-in-law's poodle against father's butcher's chihuahua. Give me sheep any day."

Weather Report

Today will be especially sunny as three suns will appear in the air.

However, gloom will descend later, especially for any descendants of Richard Duke of York.

Sons Rise
York's three lads beat the Queen's Army

The Yorkist army, led by George, Edward and Richard, sons of the Duke of York, have inflicted a crushing defeat on the Queen's forces.

Aided by Warwick's men, they forced the Queen to flee. The battle also saw off Clifford, whose head has now replaced the Duke's above the gates of York.

"I like this one even better," said a tourist. "It's especially clever the way the eyes follow you around."

Following the victory, Edward, the old Duke's eldest son, has been declared King.

"I shall reunite the land, forge an alliance with France and capture the ex-King and Queen. And in the afternoon I think I'll go for a walk."

Shades of Grey

The newly crowned King Edward has married Lady Grey, a war widow he met in court. "They make a lovely couple," said a palace spokesman. "It's a real love match."

Warwick

The wedding, however, flies in the face of advice given by Warwick. "Warwick has gone to France to secure a bride for the King and seal an alliance," said a diplomatic correspondent.

"This move completely undermines him. I don't think he's going to be a happy bunny."

WHO'S GOT WHO?

The Bard's Handy War Guide

Confused by what's going on in the country?
Can't tell who is on which side? Here's the state of play.

Edward IV

He defeated Margaret and claimed the throne.

He captured Henry who then escaped.

He was captured by Warwick but then escaped.

Currently: At Barnet, about to battle Warwick's forces.

George, Duke of Clarence

After Edward married he defected.

Then he cleaned it up and went to join Warwick.

Released King Henry from the Tower.

Went to relieve Warwick.

Cleared that up as well.

At the siege of Coventry he was persuaded to rejoin his brothers Edward and Richard.

Currently: At Barnet, busy with a mop.

Henry VI

After drifting aimlessly around he was grabbed by the gamekeepers. He was then sent to the Tower of London, but released by George, Duke of Clarence and escaped...

...Only to be captured again at Coventry.

Currently: Reading a book back in the Tower again.

Richard, Duke of Gloucester

Escaped from Warwick's army, then helped Edward escape.

Went to the osteopath.

Captured Henry at Coventry.

Currently: At Barnet, presenting a TV show entitled 'Villainy for Beginners'.

Queen Elizabeth (née Lady Grey)

Married Edward while Warwick was away.

Currently: Doing a tapestry somewhere.

Warwick

Went to France to secure a bride for Edward.

When Edward married Lady Grey, he came back from France.

With an army.

In a mood.

Captured Edward, but let him escape.

Currently: At Barnet, about to fight Edward.

Queen Margaret

Went to France to get reinforcements.

Did some shopping, took in a few shows then invaded the country.

Currently: heading towards Tewkesbury 'as there's a good sale on'.

Lord Tarquin of Chelsea

Did the interior design for the tents at Coventry.

Currently: Doing a tapestry somewhere.

I'M HENRY THE LATE, I AM!

EXCLUSIVE

King Henry Killed

Warwick Dead

Prince Murdered

Henry's troubled reign came to a brutal and bloody end as he was murdered in the Tower yesterday.

According to rumours, he was despatched by Richard, Duke of Gloucester; the hunchbacked brother of King Edward IV.

Defeated

Henry's army was soundly defeated at Barnet. Warwick was killed and his son, Prince Edward, was stabbed to death by the three sons of York. His wife, Queen Margaret, has been exiled to France.

"I think we can say it's not been the best of months for Henry," said a source.

Crookback

The King met his end at the hands of Richard, the new King's youngest brother.

Richard has long had a reputation for being an unforgiving foe.

"I think it comes from his disabilities," said a source. "I mean for a start, he has this hunch. All his shirts have to be ironed over a wok.

"But he's always been a weird boy. According to rumours he was even born with teeth and dogs bark at him as he goes by. He was sent into this breathing world scarce half made up, if you ask me."

Enthusiastic

Richard himself was enthusiastic about the new regime.

"Now is the winter of our discontent made glorious summer, by this son of York," he said. "The sun has got his hat on, hip-hip-hip hooray."

The new king has promised a time of peace.

"We have all had enough killing," he said. "I think we need to settle down. There will be no more deaths. And I promise you my brothers feel the same."

DEAD DRUNK

Clarence drowns in vat of wine

George, Duke of Clarence, has been found dead in a barrel of wine.

The wine, a butt of Malmsey, was in the Tower of London, where the Duke was imprisoned.

He had been put in the Tower following the King's suspicions that George was trying to overthrow him.

"Say what you like, but it's a great way to go," said one of the people who found him. "It's just a shame it wasn't a better vintage. Still, fancy a drink?"

The King is reported to be filled with remorse about the event.

"I know he signed a death warrant," said a courtier. "But he changed his mind just afterwards. I don't know how this happened. It must be some form of clerical error."

Dear Lady Marge

Dear Lady Marge
Can you help me? I am being woo'd by one of the three men who killed my husband.

My late husband was a young Prince and heir to the throne, who was brutally stabbed to death.

Now one of the three men who stabbed him is asking me to marry him.

What is more, he is physically handicapped and morally repugnant.

The last time we met I spat at him, yet still I find myself fancying him. What should I do?
Yours
Lady A.

Dear Lady A.
It's the same old story. A young princess, on the rebound after her husband is assassinated, falls for the hunch-backed, smooth-talking bloke who did her husband in.

Does he really love you? Or is he merely after a trophy bride?

If you ask me spitting was the right move.
Love
Lady Marge

DEADWARD THE FOURTH

Edward dies
Richard is Protector

King Edward is dead.

Although he had been ill for some time, it appears that his end was hastened by the unfortunate death of his brother, George, Duke of Clarence.

"I think Edward was heart-broken by what happened to his brother," said a source. "Although he signed the death warrant, he immediately rescinded it and sent another messenger. Unfortunately, the second letter was too slow. He must have put a second-class stamp on it or something."

Protector

Edward's death means that his young sons are next in line.

"As they are so young I will be looking after them personally," said Richard, Duke of Gloucester. "They need someone to take care of them, to make sure they don't do anything silly, like playing hopscotch on the battle-ments or anything like that."

Rumours

There have even been rumours that the young Princes are not true heirs.

"It would be unfair to the young lads to question their parentage," said Buckingham, Richard's press officer. "But let's face it, Edward didn't half put himself about a bit. Frankly we're not sure of his legitimacy either."

"That is a heinous slur," said the Duchess of York, Edward's mother. "Richard is just trying to get his hands on the throne. I'm scared for those boys.

"Who is going to protect them from the Lord Protector?"

For Hire
Discontented gentleman
for hire
All kinds of villainy considered
'Problems' removed
Child-murdering our speciality
Contact Henry Tyrrel, A dark alley, London

Lords Lose Their Heads

Several senior Lords have been executed at the express order of the Lord Protector.

Lords Ratcliffe, Rivers, Grey and Vaughan were all beheaded yesterday morning.

"They were guilty of a whole range of things," said Richard. "Including treason, sedition, murder, witchcraft, grievous bodily bumping into me, wearing very bad hats and parking on a double yellow line.

"Frankly, death's too good for them."

Anne ill

Anne, wife of Richard, is ill, according to sources.

"She's never been well, since the wedding," said a source. "I think she might be allergic to homicidal maniacs."

THE IN-LAWS

Your complete cut-out-and-keep family tre

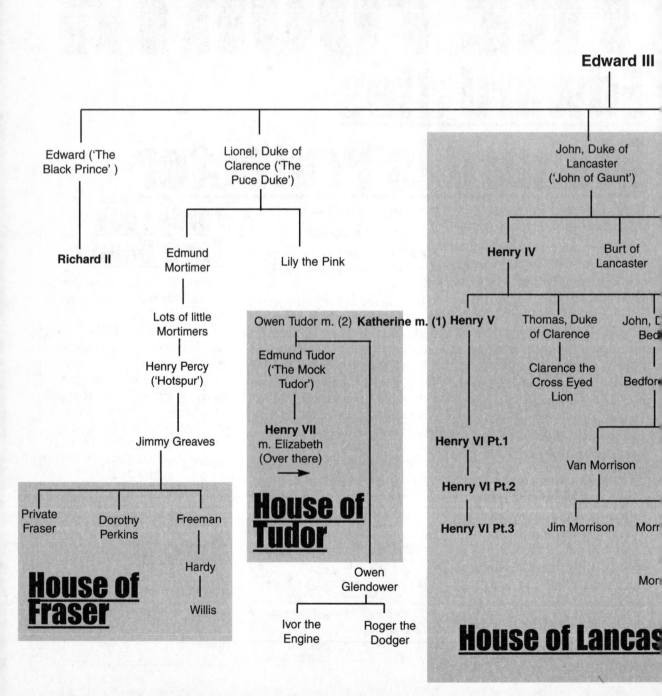

Edward III

Edward ('The Black Prince')

Lionel, Duke of Clarence ('The Puce Duke')

John, Duke of Lancaster ('John of Gaunt')

Richard II

Edmund Mortimer

Lily the Pink

Henry IV

Burt of Lancaster

Lots of little Mortimers

Owen Tudor m. (2) **Katherine m. (1) Henry V**

Thomas, Duke of Clarence

John, D Bed

Henry Percy ('Hotspur')

Edmund Tudor ('The Mock Tudor')

Clarence the Cross Eyed Lion

Bedfor

Henry VII m. Elizabeth (Over there) →

Henry VI Pt.1

Jimmy Greaves

Van Morrison

House of Tudor

Henry VI Pt.2

Private Fraser

Dorothy Perkins

Freeman

Henry VI Pt.3

Jim Morrison

Morr

Hardy

Owen Glendower

House of Fraser

Willis

Ivor the Engine

Roger the Dodger

Morr

House of Lancas

OF THE ROSES

all the recent Kings and Queens of England

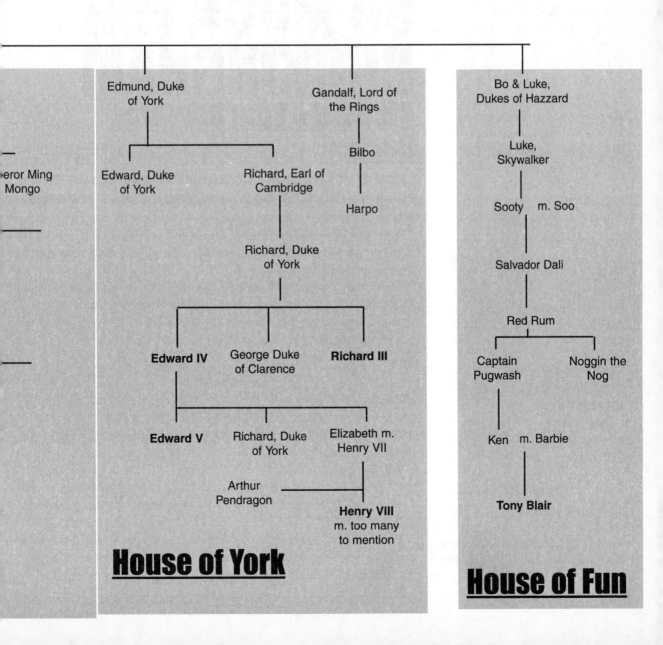

eror Ming
Mongo

Edmund, Duke
of York

Edward, Duke
of York

Richard, Earl of
Cambridge

Gandalf, Lord of
the Rings

Bilbo

Harpo

Richard, Duke
of York

Edward IV   George Duke
of Clarence   **Richard III**

Edward V   Richard, Duke
of York   Elizabeth m.
Henry VII

Arthur
Pendragon

Henry VIII
m. too many
to mention

House of York

Bo & Luke,
Dukes of Hazzard

Luke,
Skywalker

Sooty   m. Soo

Salvador Dali

Red Rum

Captain
Pugwash   Noggin the
Nog

Ken   m. Barbie

Tony Blair

House of Fun

WHERE ARE THE PRINCES?

'What has happened to the young Princes?'

That's the question on the lips of virtually every Londoner, as Richard set about having himself crowned King yesterday.

"Never mind about them," said Richard at a packed press conference. "We know they are probably illegitimate anyway.

"Have me as King instead. I may not be beautiful, but I'm effective."

Support

An early poll, however, reveals that Richard is less popular than he thinks.

"He hasn't got much support," said an observer. "Which is surprising when you think how much else is physically wrong with him."

Despite their hesitancy, the Duke looks set to become King Richard III.

The Mayor of London has offered him the crown. Despite appearing reluctant, he has agreed.

Questions

The questions still remain about the fate of the Princes in the Tower. In answer to questions Richard replied "Don't you worry – they're being taken care of."

SO MUCH FOR BUCKINGHAM
Richard's Spin Doctor is Sacked

Lord Buckingham, former PR adviser to King Richard III, has been sacked, it was revealed today.

The dispute is thought to have originated over Richard's refusal to grant an Earldom to Buckingham, the man widely held responsible for Richard's meteoric rise.

There are rumours that the pair also fell out over a request from Richard for Buckingham to "deal with" the Princes in the Tower.

"Buckingham may be a double-dealing, conniving, lying, cheating scumbag, but he's got his principles," said an inside source. "He refused to have anything to do with it."

Richmond

Buckingham is thought to have allied himself with Henry Richmond, the last representative of the house of Lancaster, who is preparing to invade from France. The late Henry VI was Richmond's uncle. Or possibly his nephew. Or maybe his mother-in-law.

"It's terribly confusing," said a source. "All the direct heirs have been killed off. Now we're dealing with the real small twigs of the family tree." Richmond is thought to want to marry Anne, daughter of Edward IV.

"He wants to depose Richard, unite the Lancaster and York houses and lead us all out of this mess," said a friend. "All I hope is that he's had plenty of Weetabix this morning."

Buckingham Dies

Richard III has executed Buckingham without trial.

"I know he wanted to spread certain lies about me," said Richard, "so I thought it best just to get rid of him."

"It gave me no pleasure killing an old friend," the King said. "Well, not much pleasure anyhow."

Mystic Mog

News from beyond the grave for Richard.

On the eve of the battle of Bosworth, we asked Mystic Mog, the old Crone of Coventry, to contact the dead and get their comments on Richard.

Here's what she said:

"I heard from many ghosts. First, Prince Edward told him to 'despair and die'. Then Henry VI repeated the message. Clarence, on the other hand, told him to 'despair and die'.

"By now I was spotting a pattern. So I was not surprised when Hastings, Rivers and all that lot told Richard to 'despair and die'.

"He got the same message from all the ghosts – Lady Anne, the young Princes, Banquo, Hamlet's Father, and the Ghost of Christmas Past."

So what does Mystic Mog think of these spirit-messages?

"Oh, I think they were probably exaggerating," she said cheerfully. "After all, ghosts can't be that clever can they? If they were that clever they wouldn't be dead."

RICHARD SHOUTS HIMSELF "HORSE"

Tricky Dicky Dies At Bosworth
Richmond is Henry VII

Richard III died yesterday at the battle of Bosworth Field.

He fought a desperate, almost valiant, fight against his enemies, refusing to give in even when his horse was cut from underneath him.

"He phoned me up during the battle and shouted 'My Kingdom for a horse', but we were fresh out," said a pet shop owner. "I offered him a hamster, but he wasn't interested."

"He'd not slept well," explained an observer. "And he was struggling to keep his alliance together. He kidnapped Lord Stanley's son, to make him co-operate, but that didn't work. In the end, everything just fell apart."

Crowned

Stanley took the crown from the dead King's head and offered it to Henry Richmond.

"Well, there's hardly any royalty left, is there," he said. "I mean, after Richmond there's a semi-senile fifth cousin and the palace cat. So I think he's the best choice really."

Villain

So ends the career of one of England's worst villains.

"He always acted as if the audience was watching," said a courtier. "I don't know what it was, he just loved playing parts. But in the end, when he took all the masks off, it was like there was nothing there. He was the greatest actor of his age."

Do You Want To Be King?

Everyone knows that Warwick the Kingmaker is the most powerful man in the country. Here, at last, we show you the form that all prospective monarchs have to fill in.

Earl of Warwick
Administrative Office, Warwick Castle

Dear **Mr Plantagenet**
Thank you for your enquiry about becoming a King of England.
  In order to process your application we need to ask you a few questions. Please answer all questions and try not to lie, unless you are Richard of Gloucester.
  Please note that the English monarchy is an equal opportunities employer. Apart from the fact that no foreigners are allowed.

OFFICIAL APPLICATION FORM

Write on one side of the paper and don't forget to draw your coat of arms.

Name:...
Earldom or Duchy:...............................

Age 0-9 months ☐
     1-15 ☐
     16-35 ☐
     36-50 ☐
     Very Old Indeed ☐
     Margaret of Anjou ☐

Are you a
Plantagenet ☐ Tudor ☐
Glendower ☐ Neville ☐
Beauchamp ☐ Mortimer ☐
Confused ☐ Cade ☐
Cholmondley-Montmorency ☐
Other........................ *(Please specify)*

Have you ever had any of the following?
Black Death ☐ Scrofula ☐
Pox ☐ Ague ☐

How do you propose to deal with your family?
Drown in wine ☐ Exile ☐
Grant earldoms ☐ Imprison ☐
Throw off battlements ☐
Marry ☐

Do you know who the last King was?
Richard ☐ Henry ☐
Part 1 ☐ Edward ☐
Northward ☐ Eastward Ho ☐
Margaret ☐ Bernard ☐
Bolingbroke ☐ Hotspur ☐
Another.....................................

What would you do with France?
Invade ☐ Visit ☐
Ignore ☐ Purchase ☐

Have you ever been on a Crusade?
Yes ☐ No ☐
No, but I go to church at Christmas ☐

Tie-breaker – Complete in 25 words or less
I want to be the next monarch because
....
....

THE GHOST OF A GREAT DANE

Sentries See Weird Apparition

EXCLUSIVE

Two sentries have reported seeing the ghost of the late King, walking the battlements of Elsinore Castle.

"It was an uncanny likeness," said Horatio (25). "He looked exactly as he did when he smote the sledded Polacks on the ice. I.e. not very happy."

Marcellus, another witness of the apparition, told us, "Thrice he walked by within his truncheon's length. Which is a clever trick, whichever way you look at it."

Beaver

"He wore his beaver up," said Horatio. "Which, I ought to point out, is a face-guard, and not a large, wood-eating rodent. I mean no one goes around with a rodent on their face do they? Although I once had a friend with a mole."

Depression

This apparition will upset young Prince Hamlet, who has been suffering from depression ever since his father pegged out.

"He mooches around the castle, muttering to himself all day long," said one observer.

"His mother is at her wits' end. She's suggested all kinds of activities – macramé, needle-work, single combat, invading Latvia. But he's just not interested."

Others were less concerned. "He's just a typical student," said a friend. "He'll be playing Leonard Cohen records next."

BARD GOSSIP

Happiness Is A Prince Called Hamlet

Rumours of a wedding abound as Prince Hamlet is seen in company with Ophelia, daughter of Polonius.

"Of course, I am not at liberty to say anything," said Polonius. "But the Prince is certainly a charming young man. I believe he has made many tenders of his affection, as it were."

News From University

Meanwhile Laertes, brother of Ophelia, has returned to university in France, where he is expected to study the three 'r's': reading, rioting and revenge tragedies.

"I was going to get a student loan," he told us, "But Dad said, 'neither a borrower or a lender be'. So I must live within my means. Which is a pain for a student."

Wild Parties At The Palace

Stories of wild parties and all-night drinking sessions at the palace have been strongly denied by royal authorities.

"There is absolutely no truth in the assershin... asstartion... claim that King Claudius has been knocking back the Rhenish wine. These accusations of drunkenness are disgusting. Now, if you'll excuse me, I think I need to go and have a lie down."

THE BARD SAYS

Queen Gertrude – Our View

Some people have been questioning the haste with which Queen Gertrude married her ex-husband's brother.

Various words and phrases have been used, including 'indecent', 'possibly incestuous' and 'complete slapper'.

Certainly the arrangement was unusual.

But we here at the Bard like to think that Denmark is a tolerant, open society.

Why should she spend months in mourning? Isn't it depressing enough living in a country chiefly known for its bacon?

We say, 'Good luck to you, your Majesty.'

Just don't have any children.

MEANWHILE Prince Hamlet is acting like a spoilt child. Some trendy psychologists have asked us to be sympathetic towards the Prince. They say he's suffering from an advanced Oedipal complex.

Rubbish! He's just being a moody brat. He should lighten up a bit and support his family.

After all. Say what you like about Oedipus. But at least he loved his mother.

Ear Today, Gone Tomorrow

Was the death of the King all it appears? A new film by Olivier Stonesofelsinore claims that the King was assassinated, the victim of a conspiracy. "The official version claims that the King was stung by a serpent," said Olivier, "But we think they may have used hebanon, and poured it into the King's ear while he was sleeping in the orchard."

This, he claims, would explain the witnesses who heard the King yelling, 'Oh my flipping ear!' and 'Who put all these apple trees here?'

Official sources, however, have poured scorn on the film-maker's theories.

"There is really no need for all these wild conjectures," said a palace spokesman. "For a start, no-one's ever heard of hebanon. It's a totally made up name. He'll be talking about a grassy knoll and a missing car next. No, rest assured, there is nothing suspicious about the way in which the King died. Oh, and by the way, can we have this bloke's address?"

TO BE OR NOT TO BE — WHAT KIND OF QUESTION IS THAT?

Nutty Prince Bonkers Over Ophelia

Prince Hamlet is reported to be what medical experts are calling "one turret short of a castle".

In an official announcement, the Royal Doctor pronounced the Prince "clinically bonkers".

"We're very concerned about the young Prince," said the Doctor. "Something has upset him, although what it is we're not quite sure. He seems to have taken against his uncle the King in a big way and his relationship with Ophelia has fallen to pieces."

Ophelia is said to be distraught at the collapse of her romance.

"She really loved him," said a close friend. "She's taken it very hard and has started singing nonsense songs. Not that it notices much. I mean, this place has got more nuts in it than a Dundee cake."

THE OPHELIAGATE LETTERS
Were These The Love Letters That Drove The Prince Batty?

The Bard has obtained copies of the notorious Opheliagate letters. In a series of torrid outpourings, Hamlet reveals his passion for the daughter of Polonius, and later his increasing madness.

The letters paint an unsettling portrait of a young man in deep emotional turmoil. You might find them disturbing, not merely because they show a mind disintegrating, but also because the poetry is so appalling.

The poems start with a conventional expression of love.

"Doubt thou the stars are fire,
Doubt that the sun doth move,
Doubt truth to be a liar,
But never doubt I love."

However, doubt begins to creep in.

"Ophelia! Ophelia!
I am glad that you're not
  Delia!
Even though she cooks better.
And that's the end of this
  letter."

By now the Prince is clearly losing it, his poems displaying an increasing distaste for women.

"Ophelia you're a painted
  bawd,
A lisping, wanton strumpet.
Hence! Get thee to a nunnery,
And let me play my trumpet."

"There is something not right here," said a psychologist. "It's almost as if he's pretending. After all, even the completely insane have no desire to play the trumpet. They might be mad, but they're not stupid."

The Bard Theatre Review

The Mousetrap: The Murder of Gonzago
by Andrew Lloyd-Pickledherring, with additional material by Prince Hamlet.

Live from the castle courtyard, Elsinore, this spectacular new production told a tawdry tale.

A noble King enters, singing a patriotic song (*Denmark, Denmark, What a Good Standard of Living We Enjoy*). He is lured by his wife and falls asleep in a field (*Come, Lay Your Head in My Meadow*).

His nephew Lucianus enters and pours poison in the sleeping King's ear (*Ear We Go, Ear We Go, Ear We Go*). The King dies (*What's This In Ear?*) and his wife marries Lucianus who takes over the kingdom (*Fjord He's a Jolly Good Fellow*).

There are some nice touches. The singing apple trees in the orchard were endearing and the massed recorder ensemble at the end certainly left you humming the tunes.

Above all the play lacks a proper ending.

Although this could have been because the real King, and most of the audience, left in a strop halfway through.

STABBED IN THE ARRAS

"I Didn't Know Who He Was" Says Prince

EXCLUSIVE

Hamlet, the mad Prince, has killed Polonius in a tragic misunderstanding.

The Prince was in his mother's chamber when he heard a noise behind the arras.

"He thought it was an assassin," said a palace spokesman. "You mustn't forget that this is a very paranoid young man."

Attack

In fact the noise was Polonius, who thought that the Prince was about to attack his own mother. Hamlet struck with his sword through the curtain, killing the old man immediately.

"It's just one of those things," said a friend of the Prince. "It's a mistake anyone could make."

Revenge

It is reported that Laertes, the son of Polonius, has not taken the news too well and is even now on his way back to Denmark to seek revenge on the Prince.

Ophelia Takes A Dive

Ophelia, one-time fiancee of Hamlet, is dead.

Driven to distraction by her rejection, she drowned herself in a nearby stream.

"I'm heart-broken," said her brother Laertes. "I blame Hamlet. He drove her to distraction with his endless rambling."

The death comes just as Ophelia was starting to establish a successful singing career. She had already written several new songs including 'He is dead and gone, lady', 'Tomorrow is St. Valentine's Day', 'Young men will do't' and 'I've got a lovely bunch of coconuts'.

"She had a great career before her," said her agent. "Mind you, dying young is a good career move as well. It did wonders for Janis Joplin and Jim Morrison."

HAMLET IS SNUFFED OUT

EXCLUSIVE

Fencing Competition Ends In Mass Murder
King, Queen, Prince, Laertes and hamster die

The life of Hamlet, ill-fated Prince of Denmark, is over. He has died after a fencing competition went horribly wrong.

The Prince was fighting Laertes, the son of Polonius in a grudge match. Not only had Hamlet killed his father, but his sister went mad after the death of her father and her apparent rejection by Hamlet.

"Apparently one of the swords was poisoned," said an onlooker. "I think Laertes intended it to kill Hamlet. He wounded the Prince, but then the swords got swapped. Laertes died of the poison, while Gertrude died through drinking poisoned wine. Hamlet forced his uncle to drink the wine and they all died together. I tell you, some days it never rains but it pours."

Madness

The disaster brings to an end a sorry tale of madness and deceit.

"It would have been better for the Prince if he'd been able to leave things well alone. He felt like he should be the one to revenge his father's death, but he was temperamentally unsuitable for it."

"He was good at fighting, but never a real warrior. He was devoted to Ophelia, but found himself unable to trust women. He was called to take revenge, but he couldn't. In the end, it was a mess. But that's death for you."

Fortinbras Invades

Elsinore castle has been invaded by the Norwegians under Fortinbras.

The Prince arrived just as the final grisly act was reaching its conclusion.

"They've left the place in a terrible mess," said Fortinbras. "There are poisoned chalices, strange ear syringes and old skulls lying around everywhere."

Fortinbras intends to renovate the castle and open it to the public.

"I think this will become a place of pilgrimage for young, introspective people everywhere," he said.

FIRST HIS SONS, NOW HIS SON-IN-LAW

Cymbeline Exiles His Daughter's Husband

King Cymbeline has exiled his son-in-law, Posthumous Leonatus. Posthumous married Imogen, the King's daughter, against her father's wishes. Now he has been punished by exile to Italy.

"Well, it's not much of a punishment, is it?" said one courtier. "I mean all that wine and sun-dried tomatoes and all that. He'll be OK."

Loss

The move echoes the dramatic loss of the King's own sons many years ago. Arviragus and Guiderius were stolen from their cradles as infants while they were watching a Teletubbies video. They have never been seen since.

"He's obviously got this thing about sons," said a source at court. "He keeps losing them."

Hopes

The King objected to the match because he was hoping to marry his daughter to his stepson Cloten.

Cloten, the son of the present Queen, has been described as "a classic product of inbreeding" and "the strongest argument yet for a republic".

"He's not exactly Einstein," agreed a courtier. "So it's not surprising that Imogen chose to marry somebody more interesting. Then again, there are things growing under rocks that are more interesting than Cloten."

IMOGEN AND THE TRUNK CALL
Stalker Describes Night In Princess's Room

In a shocking new book, an Italian spy described today how he spent the night with Princess Imogen.

In the book he reveals his brief affair with the Princess and talks frankly and openly about their relationship.

"I only did it for a bet," said Major Iachimo, an emissary from Rome. "I know some people think I'm a cad, publishing a kiss and tell book like this. But since I don't actually have any morals I don't care."

He goes on to describe in detail the pictures and tapestries on the walls.

"She has a tapestry of Cleopatra in silver silk, and above the chimney is a carving of Diana bathing."

He also describes more personal details.

"She had a mole on her left breast," he told us. "I don't know what it was doing there but it seemed quite happy and it kept her chest warm."

The unscrupulous Italian has even taken a bracelet given to Imogen by her husband.

"I know people will say that I'm nothing more than a common thief and peeping Tom," he said. "But I think I've done everyone a service with this. I mean the security was non-existent. All I had to do to gain entry to her bedchamber was hide in a trunk."

Imogen Flees To Wales

Princess Imogen has fled the court and headed for Wales, according to informed sources.

However, uninformed sources said, "We don't know anything about it."

The Princess appears to be trying to meet up with her exiled husband Posthumous, who has landed at Milford Haven with a load of Romans. "I hope he'll be pleased to see her," said a friend.

Cloten Loses His Head

Prince Cloten has been beheaded in a fight with a mad Welshman.

According to sources, the Prince was trying to discover the whereabouts of Princess Imogen, his step-sister. It was unclear what he was after her for, although sources hint at evil desires.

"Let's just say he didn't want to play Monopoly with her," said a source. "He's always had the hots for that girl."

Conflict

His search brought him into conflict with Cadwal, a Welsh cave-dweller.

"He was right rude," said Cadwal. "He just upped and attacked me. I had no option but to cut off his head. It was self-defence."

"I carried the head back to my dad. It was quite light really. But then he didn't have much inside it."

A POSTHUMOUS PARDON
Imogen Reunited With Husband
Missing Sons Turn Up In Wales

King Cymbeline has pardoned Posthumous Leonatus after an amazing reunion.

The ageing King was reunited not only with his daughter and her husband, but also with his long-lost sons.

"There is some good news and some bad news," said a court correspondent. "The good news is that his sons Guiderius and Arviragus are alive and well. The bad news is they're Welsh."

Cave

The boys have been brought up in a cave above Milford Haven under the assumed names of Cadwal and Polydore. In a bizarre twist they recently ran into their sister Imogen when she was disguised as a boy called Fidele.

Eye-opener

"It's all been a bit of an eye-opener, really," said Arviragus. "We knew from the start there was something special about the lad, but we didn't know what. Maybe it was the bosoms. I mean, there aren't many young shepherds who are 38DD."

"You can't blame them for not realizing sooner," said Imogen. "I mean they're only used to identifying sheep. A woman is beyond their experience."

THE BARD SAYS
IACHIMO AND THE PRINCESS – AN APOLOGY

Following a decision by the Press Complaints Authority, we would like to apologize for the recent story about Iachimo and Princess Imogen.

We now accept that the story was a complete fabrication and that Iachimo never got his leg over at all, but was lying to win a bet.

In accordance with the decision of the authority we are glad to print a full apology in a prominent position in the newspaper.

You will find the full text on page 38, just between the classifieds and an advert for hair restorer.

EGEON HIS FACE

EXCLUSIVE

Syracusean Faces Death After Visiting Ephesus

Egeon, a Syracusean merchant, has been arrested. He will die unless he can pay a thousand mark fine. His crime? Simply being in the wrong place at the wrong time.

"We have a law in Ephesus that no citizen of Syracuse is allowed in the city," said the Duke of Ephesus. "It's for a number of reasons, partly hygiene, partly diplomatic, but mainly to do with blind, unthinking bigotry. We're very good at that kind of thing here."

Quest

Egeon claims to be on a quest for his son, who he lost when but an infant.

"I had two boys – twins," he told a reporter, "but one of them was lost in a shipwreck many years ago. Ever since then I have been trying to find the boy. And also his servant, another twin who was also lost."

Son

Egeon's surviving son and servant have been searching for seven years, but only this year did Egeon decide to search for himself.

"I'm sure my son wouldn't be so foolish as to come here," he said. "I just got on the wrong boat, that's all."

Law

Meanwhile, the Duke, though moved by the old man's story, has declined to pardon him.

"I can't break the law, even for someone like this," he said. "Besides, I have a very bad feeling about this. It all sounds depressingly complicated."

IMPOSTER!

A local merchant, Antipholus of Ephesus, has been turned away from his own home – because his wife thought he was already inside!

"I couldn't believe it," said the merchant. "My servant refused to allow me in. Someone's impersonating me."

He blames Ephesus's reputation as a haven for magicians.

"This place is just full of weirdos and mystics," complained Antipholus. "We have more quacks than a duck pond."

Trouble

Now Antipholus is in trouble with a local jeweller, who claims he has stolen a gold chain.

"I gave Antipholus the chain not half an hour ago," said Angelo. "Now he denies seeing it. I have no option but to call the police."

Denial

Antipholus, meanwhile, has denied any involvement in the scandal.

"I'm a respectable man," he said. "The only chain I've seen today is the one in the toilet, first thing this morning. On reflection it might have been better if I'd stayed there."

LOVE-CHEAT HUSBAND CHASES AFTER SISTER-IN-LAW

Married Man Chats Up Wife's Sister

A married merchant of Ephesus tried to seduce his own sister-in-law. What's more, he was still married at the time!

"I don't know what's got into him," said shocked Lucinda (22). "It's like he's a different man. He kept talking about how beautiful my eyes were, and how he loved me, and all the time he was married to my sister.

"I think it might be his mid-life crisis or something."

Mistaken Identity

Meanwhile, the merchant is claiming a case of mistaken identity.

"I don't know how I got into this mess," he complained. "Everyone seems to know me and my servant, but we don't know anyone. I just want to get away from this place."

Fury

His wife, however, is furious.

"The sad thing is I don't know what he thinks a young woman like my sister would see in him," she said.

"He is deformed, crooked, old, ill-faced, worse bodied and shapeless. She'd have more fun getting off with an old three-piece suite."

BROTHER, FATHER AND REVEREND MOTHER!

Family reunited as father finds mother in the abbey

They were split apart 23 years ago by a shipwreck. Now they've been brought together again by a bizarre chain of events.

The family of Egeon were separated by a shipwreck. Egeon lost his wife, Emilia, one of his sons, and one of his son's servants.

Now they have all been rediscovered in Ephesus. First the two sets of twins were reunited after a farcical series of misunderstandings in the city.

Seeing Things

"When they both walked through the door I thought I was seeing things," said Egeon. "They're so alike you simply can't tell them apart. No wonder there's been so much confusion."

But the crowning moment came when the Abbess revealed that she is in fact Egeon's long-lost wife Emilia. She had her son and his servant taken from her by Corinthian fishermen. Antipholus and Dromio returned to Ephesus, never knowing their mother had taken vows and was living in an abbey nearby.

Relief

"It's all turned out very happily," said the Syracusean Dromio, who has been reunited with his twin brother. "There was a nasty moment when it looked like I might have to marry the kitchen maid, a woman who resembles a small mountain. I'm so relieved that she is going to be my sister and not my wife."

DADDY'S GIRL
Secret revealed in deadly gameshow

Pericles, Prince of Tyre has escaped from Antioch – even though he successfully passed a challenge to gain the Princess's hand.

"The contest was a riddle," said the Prince. "But the answer revealed a hideous secret, so the King ordered my death. I thought I'd win a car. Instead they took out a contract."

Threat

The threat to his life means that the Prince has had to keep on the move, leaving his deputy to govern in Tyre.

"I can't reveal the secret, really I can't," said a shocked Prince. "Let's just say that the King and his daughter are close. Very close. As close as you can get."

According to sources, the King invented the riddle to put suitors off. If they failed to guess it, they would be killed. Pericles was the first to succeed.

"Is it my fault I'm good at riddles?" said the Prince as he escaped. "I'm being punished for being a lateral thinker."

BARD RACING

The 3.30 Tournament from Pentapolis
The Princess Thaisa Stakes
Prize: the hand of the Princess in marriage
Your Guide to The Knights

 No. 1 Sir Michael of Sparta
Motto: Lux tua vita mihi (*Have you got a light, mate?*)

 No. 2 Prince Alan of Macedon
Motto: Più e per dolcezza che per forza (*A tub of Dolcelatte for four please.*)

 No. 3 Sir Anthony of Antioch
Motto: Me pompae provexit apex (*For me, Up Pompeii was the best thing on TV.*)

 No. 4 Sir Cynthia of Purley
Motto: Qui me alit, me extinguit (*In case of fire, break glass.*)

 No. 5 Sir Gazza of Newcastle
Motto: Sic spectanda fides (*Are you looking at me?*)

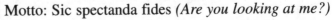
 No. 6 Sir Anonymous of Anonymous Town
Motto: In hac spe vivo (*All journalists drink wine.*)

FOR THOSE IN PERICLES ON THE SEA

BARD EXCLUSIVE

Prince Pericles has lost his wife in a shipwreck

Princess Thaisa, who gave birth on board the ship, was laid in a sealed coffin and floated out to sea during the storm.

"It's what she would have wanted," said an observer. "She was always keen on swimming."

The young daughter, named Marina, has been left at Tarsus in the care of King Cleon and Queen Dionyza.

"She's such a fragile little thing, I don't think she will survive another voyage," said Pericles. "I'll leave her here for a bit. Say sixteen years or so."

The King was returning with his new bride to his old job of governing Tyre.

"I had hoped that my queen would be with me," he said. "But she is gone. I'll never see her again."

However, one spectator disagreed.

"Stranger things have happened," he said. "Most notably in *The Winter's Tale*."

OUT OF THE FRYING PAN
Pirates steal Marina
"She was going to be killed anyway" says assassin

Marina (16), the daughter of Pericles, has been stolen by pirates.

The shock event occurred when she was taken to a beach to be killed by an assassin.

"Honestly, this place is getting so lawless," said Leonine the assassin. "You can't even murder somebody these days without criminals getting involved."

Popularity

The teenager had been singled out for murder because of her popularity.

"She's such a wonderful person that she overshadows the daughter of the Queen," said a spokesman. "Which is not very tactful when you come to think of it."

Informed sources said that she will probably be sold into prostitution. Uninformed sources said, "For heaven's sake stop asking me all these questions."

News of the kidnapping has been sent to Pericles.

"Well, we've not exactly said 'kidnapping'," explained a palace spokesman. "We've more said 'died of natural causes'. After all, he's not seen her for years, so he's not going to be that bothered, is he?"

Poisoned

After a poisoning attempt, Leonine the assassin was reported to be stable yesterday.

"He's dead, actually," said a doctor. "But you can't get much more stable than that, can you?"

In a note, Leonine wrote: "What did I tell you about all these criminals?"

Brothels Report Recession

Business is bad for the brothel owners according to the latest report.

"Business is dropping off alarmingly," said a Mytilene owner. "Never mind Viagra, it's more like Niagara out there."

They are blaming the decline on "faulty merchandise".

"We bought this new girl from a load of pirates," said one owner. "She's a great looker, but she won't sleep with any of the blokes. Instead, she just talks to them and they decide to change their ways and lead virtuous lives."

The Bard spoke to one of her clients.

"I am out of the road of rutting forever," he said.

ANOTHER HAPPY ENDING

BARD EXCLUSIVE

Pericles, Marina, Thaisa reunited

Pericles has been reunited with the daughter and wife he thought were dead.

The first reunion – with his daughter Marina – occurred in Mytilene, where she had been taken by pirates.

"I first met her in a brothel," said Lysimachus, Lord of Mytilene. "Not that I was using it myself, of course. No, this was a sort of royal walkabout kind of thing. I was testing her virtue. Honestly."

Education

Marina persuaded the brothel owner to release her from the bawdy-house and set up an adult education project for the people of Mytilene.

"It's been great," she said. "We've done wine-making, conversational Greek and GCSE Rhetoric."

"It's all very well," said the brothel owner. "But I still say she would have made a lot more people happy my way."

When Pericles arrived on a royal visit, he believed that his daughter was dead. However a chance remark brought her to his boat and they soon realized that they were related.

"It's wonderful to see Daddy again," said Marina. "Well, I say 'again'. I've never seen him before."

"I meant to write," said Pericles. "But you know how busy you get as a King."

Diana

The two decided to go to Ephesus to give thanks to Diana. And it was there that they received their next shock.

The priestess who officiated at the thanksgiving was Thaisa, Pericles' long lost wife.

"I thought he'd never find me... I mean, I thought he was dead." she said. "I've spent years building a career as a vestal virgin, and now he turns up again. Talk about a fairy-tale ending."

Dear Auntie Bard...

In a fix? Need advice? Then write to Auntie Bard, your very own agony Aunt.

Dear Auntie Bard,

I am a young orphan. My father was a famous physician and I know that I am well regarded at Court. However, I am in love with Bertram, the son of the Count. He is a terrible snob and looks down on me. How will I ever make this match?
Yours,
Helena

Dear Helena

Are you sure you want to marry him? Why not join the Socialist Workers Party, organise a revolution and have him shot instead? You might find it more fulfilling.

However, assuming that you do want to marry him, my advice is as follows:

All the best
Auntie Bard

Dear Auntie Bard,

I took your advice and got him, but now he's run off to Italy. (He says he's gone to fight in a war, but Italians don't have wars do they? Unless you count the football matches.)
Anyway, now he's written to me to say that he will never accept me as his wife until I am pregnant by him and wear the ring from his finger.
Now what do I do?
Yours,
Helena

Dear Helena

Piece of cake. Disguise yourself as a pilgrim and follow him. Find out a girl who he is trying to seduce (there is bound to be one) and take her place. Sleep with him, get hold of the ring and Robert is your mother's brother. Trust me, it never fails.

All the best
Auntie Bard

Dear Auntie Bard,

Please help me, I am desperate. An awfully common girl called Helena has managed to snare me by curing the King. I don't want to be married to a doctor. You never know where they've been putting their hands.
What shall I do?
Yours,
Bertram

Dear Bertram,

Don't knock being married to a doctor. You can jump the queue for hip operations for a start. Still, my advice is to run away. Assuming you have married this girl, leave for war in Italy. Then write to her setting some unrealistic conditions to her ever properly marrying you.
And hey presto! Bob is the husband of your aunt.
All the best
Auntie Bard

Dear Auntie Bard,

It's all going pear shaped! I heard that Helena was dead, so I came home to marry someone more befitting my status. What do I discover but the girl I thought I got off with in Italy was actually Helena! And now she is pregnant and has got my ring. What on earth am I to do?
Yours,
Bertram

Dear Bertram,

Just give up, dear. Accept that you have lost, make the best of it and Claudius is your Uncle*! All will be well. You will find happiness and contentment. Or not. As if I care.
All the best
Auntie Bard

*Assuming you're Hamlet

WHAT'S ON...

Your Guide to the Best TV

8.00 TIMONTUBBIES
A children's programme with the wacky creatures who store money in their stomachs.

9.00 READY STEADY DISMEMBER
With Titus Andronicus
In this fun-packed cookery programme, Titus demonstrates new ways to cook 'wood-roasted nephew' and 'heir to throne stuffed with pound of flesh'.

10.00 BLUE PETRUCHIO
How to care for your doublet, and how to build an attractive codpiece out of that old hubcap and a few lolly sticks.

11.00 PET RESCUE
This week, the presenters have to cope with a bear running amok in the wings of a theatre, and a snake which has inadvertently been put down someone's dress!

12.00 NEWS AND WEATHER
Presented by Prospero from Tempest Isle.

12.30 MUCH ADO AROUND NOONTIME
Beatrice and Benedick invite you to share an afternoon of chat, witty repartee and a lot of barely disguised innuendo. Today's guest is Malvolio who will be talking about his new book, *Stocking Fillers, The Life of A Fashion Pioneer.*

3.00 CHANGING TOMBS
Antony and Cleopatra show you how to transform your pyramid into a magnificent mausoleum.

4.00 MIDSUMMER NIGHT'S THEATRE
Straight from the wedding of Theseus and Hippolyta, we present the Rude Mechanicals in Pyramus and Thisbe, directed by Tarquin Quententino.
In this reworked version, when Thisbe is eaten by a lion, Pyramus goes mad and shoots most of ancient Athens in a bloodbath. Stars Bottom as Mr Ass, Quince as Professor Plum, Snout as First Drugdealer, and Snug as the deranged psychopathic lion.

7.00 INTERNATIONAL LOTTERY FROM VENICE
What's in the box? Another contestant gets the chance to choose numbers from the lead, bronze or gold box. The winner gets to keep most of his chest intact.

8.00 ANY QUESTIONS
Tonight's panel of experts considers the burning issues, such as 'Wherefore art thou Romeo?','Tell me where is fancy bred?' and 'Why aren't clowns actually funny?'

8.30 RIDDLE-ME-RE
See preview

9.00 SPORTSNIGHT
With Demetrius Lysander
Featuring live wrestling from the Forest of Arden, plus fencing from Denmark, and horse racing from Bosworth Field.

11.00 LATE NIGHT MOVIE
Titus Andronicus 4: The Food Processor.

12.30 THE WITCHING HOUR
Tonight's spells, prognostications and hauntings.
Presented by Puck with special appearances from Hecate, Hymen and Jupiter.

Preview

8.30 Riddle-Me-Re
This week it is Pericles' turn to have a guess at the King of Antioch's dark secret.
In a tense final we will see whether Pericles can win the woman or pay the price.
If he guesses incorrectly, of course, he will be killed. Whereas if he guesses correctly he will be assassinated.
So it's all to play for in the grand final.

BARD SPORTS

All the Action All the Time

EXILED!
Management Team Sacked

Duke Senior and his entire management team have been ousted from court, following a takeover battle led by the Duke's younger brother, Duke Ferdinand.

"The shareholders were not happy with the way the club was going," said Duke Ferdinand. "It was felt that a move would be beneficial for all parties."

Duke Senior is reported to have moved to Forest of Arden FC, a small club in the West Midlands Rural Idyll League.

Redundancies

Several of his management team have joined him already, and Duke Ferdinand has indicated that still further job losses are on the cards.

"There are several people on the playing staff here that are surplus to requirements," he said. "Including a couple of women, a moody bloke and an extremely unfunny jester.

"It's time we had a clear out."

Bung!
Scandal mars wrestling match

Charles "The Python", Duke Frederick's wrestling champion was dramatically defeated yesterday.

His opponent was Orlando de Boys, who saw off the previous world champion in the first round.

"I used the Boston Crab, a half-nelson, a whole nelson and the full monty," said Orlando. "There was no way he was coming back from that."

Orlando claims to have learned wrestling out of boredom.

"My brother won't have me educated, so there's not much else to do," he said.

Rigged

But the victory has been marred by accusations that the fight was supposed to be rigged.

"Orlando's brother set it up so that the boy would be killed," said an anonymous source. "As it is, the new champ has had to go into hiding."

Charles was reputed to be promised a large reward if he killed his opponent.

"He was promised a significant bung," said a source. "However, before he could collect it, Orlando bunged him over a hedge."

ARDEN-ED CRIMINALS
Rosalind, Orlando and others run to the Forest

Yet more people have been banished from the court. And they have all headed to the Forest of Arden, to join up with the exiled Duke Senior.

The latest expulsions include Rosalind, daughter of the old Duke, her best friend Celia and Oliver, eldest son of Sir Roland De Boys.

"Pretty soon the new Duke isn't going to have anyone left to expel," said a witness. "The words 'rats' and 'sinking ship' spring to mind."

In the forest the old Duke is reported to be living the "life of Robin Hood".

"I think that means we'll be eating venison and living in trees," said Rosalind. "As long as I don't have to wear Lincoln Green I don't mind. It's really not my colour."

Just Lion Around!
Oliver saved from certain death

The two feuding de Boys brothers have been reunited following a dramatic escape from death.

Oliver was attacked by a snake. It was frightened off by the arrival of his brother Orlando who then fought with a lion to save his brother's life.

"It's been one of those days," said a tired Orlando. "I was tempted to leave the snake to do its work, after all that Oliver's done to me, but in the end I relented."

Reunited

Orlando's act has brought the brothers together again.

"I owe him my life," said a relieved Oliver. "From now on, everything I have is his."

Baffled

Experts, however, were baffled by the day's events.

"I can't understand where these animals came from," said a zoologist. "This is the Forest of Arden. On the whole you don't get many lions in the West Midlands."

THE BARD
Behind the Big Oak
All the way round the
Mulberry Bush
Forest of Arden

SO THAT'S THE WAY YOU LIKE IT

Multiple marriages as lovers link-up

The Forest of Arden was abuzz with festivities yesterday as its inhabitants celebrated a mass wedding.

The happy couples were married by the Duke Senior, who celebrated the fact that he was once again in charge.

"This is a great day," he said. "My evil brother has become a monk, the De Boys brothers have got married and that moody old idiot Jaques has decided to join the Trappists."

Mistake

But the marriages nearly didn't take place due to a case of mistaken identity.

Rosalind, the fiancé of Orlando had disguised herself as a boy, and found herself expected to marry two people.

"As Rosalind I wanted to marry Orlando," she told us, "but as Ganymede, I was also supposed to be marrying Phebe the shepherdess. It was hilarious. Well, quite funny. All right, moderately amusing."

Sheep dip

"I'm glad she finds it funny," said the jilted shepherdess. "It's all right for her, she still got her Orlando. I've ended up with a half-wit who thinks that sheep dip is an acceptable aftershave substitute."

Meanwhile, Oliver de Boys married Celia and Touchstone the jester married a goatherd called Audrey.

"Now she's the one I feel sorry for," said Phebe. "Frankly, I think she'd have more laughs marrying the goat."

Conversion

The events were crowned with the news that the evil Duke Ferdinand had been converted to monasticism by a chance encounter with a hermit.

"He was on his way to kill everyone when he met this Holy Man," said an observer. "The upshot is that he's joined the Moonies, or Hare Krishna or something. Anyway, he's shaved his head and renounced the world.

"So that's all right then."

BARD SPORTS

All the Action All the Deeds

BEWARE OF GREEKS BEARING SHARP SWORDS

Crunch time once again for the two sides

The ongoing cup final between the Greeks and Trojans reaches its head this week in yet another replay.

Well, I say 'final'. The fact is that for ten years these two sides have been playing a war of attrition. But with the latest challenge from Hector, the signs are that the Trojans may be trying to break the impasse.

"It's been a classic case of irresistible force meeting immovable object," said Homer, our war correspondent. "The Trojans have a great defence, the Greeks a potentially devastating attack. Neither side has given way."

Star

The Greeks, particularly, have suffered from a number of splits inside the camp, with Achilles and Agamemnon at logger-heads.

"Achilles is the star, there's no doubt," said Homer. "But he's been refusing to attend training for some years now. It's all to do with some kind of bonus payment or something."

Now, with Hector's challenge, the deadlock may well be broken.

"I wouldn't bet on it," said Homer. "This one could run and run."

Trojans v Greeks

Troy 3pm Tickets **Still Available** (21 drachmas)
Match Odds Troy **3-1** Greece **2-1** Draw **Evens**
Leading Scorer Greeks **Achilles 321** Trojans **Hector 210**
Referee Mars, God of War (Olympus)

Subs from Doner, Kebab, Aristophanes

Subs from Helen of Troy, Helen Earth, Helen Mirren

"Love-Sick" Prince Troilus

Prince Troilus is, in his own words, "doubtful" for today's game.

"Why should I war without the walls of Troy that find such cruel battle here within?" he asked a baffled press conference.

"I think the lad is a little love-sick," said his agent Pandarus. "It's nothing a night of passion followed by a sudden betrayal won't cure."

His problems have led to harsh words from player-manager King Priam.

"He's got to get his head together soon," he said. "Otherwise he's likely to get it chopped off."

Meanwhile, the Trojans have identified a potentially fatal weakness in Achilles, Greece's star striker.

"We think the lad is vulnerable around the box," said Hector. "Or possibly a bit lower."

SWAPSIES
Greeks swap Antenor for Cressida

The Greeks have released the prisoner Antenor, in exchange for Cressida.

The move reunites Cressida with her father Calchas, who has joined the Greeks.

When asked if he had defected, Calchas said, "Not at all. Everything's working fine... Oh I'm sorry, I thought you said defective."

Cressida is thought to have agreed reluctantly to the move, as she was beginning an affair with Troilus.

"I'm only doing this for Daddy's sake, and for the return of Antenor," she said. "I intend to remain faithful to Troilus for the rest of my life. Or at least until Thursday."

Reports have already filtered back to Troy that she has struck up a relationship with the Greek Diomedes.

"One look at his balalaika and that was it," said a shocked Troilus. "She's betrayed me. If Helen's face could launch a thousand ships, then hers could sink a fleet."

Hector Dies
But stalemate continues

EXCLUSIVE

Hector is dead, treacherously slain by Achilles and a group of soldiers. The Trojan warrior was ambushed when he was trying on a new set of armour.

"He was caught by the Myrmidons," said an eyewitness, "which as everyone knows is a group of Greek soldiers and not a cheap double entendre. Well, alright, it is a cheap double entendre as well, but you know what I mean."

Bitter

The Trojans are particularly bitter about the death, since only a few moments earlier, Hector had let Achilles off.

"He had the Greek down on the ground, but let him off because he was unarmed," said Paris. "But then when Achilles found him unarmed he just hacked him down."

The Greeks were unrepentant.

"This is war," said Ulysses, "not some kind of parlour game. If we have to use deceitful, underhand tricks to win, then that's what we'll do."

Dragged

Following his victory, Achilles tied the body of Hector to the back of his horse and dragged it around the walls of the city.

"There was no need to do that," said an observer. "It was just showing off. He could have just taken a bow like everyone else."

When asked if the death changes things the observer said, "No, not really. We're back where we started. Nothing has changed. but then nothing ever does."

Hector leaves behind a wife, Zsa-Zsa and a next door neighbour, Fifi the frog.

BARD MONEY

Rialto Interest Rate Rise
Shipping crisis blamed

Following large scale losses to shipping, interest rates have started to rise in Venice.

"Yesterday morning I could have got you 4.75%," said one merchant banker. "But now you're looking at a couple of fingers and an ear, minimum."

Rates for larger sums such as 3,000 ducats are now being calculated in limbs, and other vital organs. The scheme was invented by Shylock Merchant Bankers, who have taken a pound of flesh as security on a loan to Antonio.

Supply And Demand

"I'm simply reacting to the market," said Shylock, whose firm pioneered the new "Pound of Flesh Bond Scheme". "Antonio needed the money and I created special terms. It's a simple case of supply and demand. Not to mention bigotry and revenge."

Response

Now, other banks are responding to the new innovative methods.

"We are investigating a range of security for loans," said Signor Tubal of the Belmont Bank. "For small loans, we are willing to take part of the family pet. We have a mid-range scheme which is secured against 50% of your grandmother. For large loans we will require a lung. Or even two."

Antonio Export Post A Loss

The Antonio Export & Import Inc. have been badly hit. All five of their ships are reported as missing at sea.

"The problem lies in the far east," said an expert. "You know, Greece, Turkey, that sort of area. Antonio has taken a real hammering as a result.

"It leaves him badly exposed. Well, his chest is badly exposed, anyway."

Antonio met with the board of directors today and declared that he would be taking action.

"Obviously there will need to be cuts," he said. "It's just a question of whether I can have anaesthetic or not."

LIKE A THIEF IN THE NIGHT

Jew's daughter elopes with his cash

Jessica, daughter of Shylock, has eloped with Lorenzo. What's more she's taken with her two bags of her father's jewellery, cash and valuables.

"She has left Venice and gone into hiding," said Tubal, who has been looking for the girl on behalf of her father. "But we are beginning to trace her by her credit card statements."

A distraught Shylock has reported it to the police.

"He did come and see us," said the Chief Inspector. "But all he could say was 'My daughter! Oh my ducats!' which wasn't particularly helpful."

Blow

The elopement will come as a bitter blow to a man already alienated by his treatment at the hands of Venetian merchants and his impending lawsuit.

"I think it makes a lawsuit against Antonio more likely," said an observer. "He feels it is just another injustice. He's been stabbed in the back. So he's probably going to take the opportunity to stab someone else in the front."

Spending

Jessica, who will also convert to Christianity, has been reported to be on a spending spree up and down the coast.

"She's been buying all kinds of things," said Tubal. "At one shop she bought a pet monkey, paying for it with a ring. Unfortunately the ring was her father's wedding ring, which he treasured all his life. I don't think even love can justify that sort of behaviour."

Hell

Others, however, were less sympathetic.

"I don't think that girl's had an easy life," said one friend of the family. "In fact she described her home as a living hell.

"I know Shylock has had his share of injustice, but even so he is an avaricious, grasping businessman.

"He's so mean he makes Scrooge look like Mother Teresa."

Revenge

It now seems clear that Shylock will pursue his revenge against Antonio. Following the merchant's inability to repay the loan, he has been arrested and charged.

The case will be heard at the Court of Law tomorrow.

"I'll be bringing my Stanley knife," said Shylock.

SORRY – FLESH IS OFF!

Shylock loses court case and half his goods

BARD EXCLUSIVE

In a dramatic twist of events, Shylock the Jew lost his court case against Antonio.
Instead it was Shylock who was fined. Half of all his possessions were confiscated and he was forced to become a Christian.

The barrister representing Antonio agreed that Shylock was legally entitled to a pound of flesh. But he would be criminally responsible if he took any blood, or any amount more than the exact pound.

Argument

"It was a brilliant piece of legal argument," said an admiring lawyer. When asked whether it was a just verdict he said, "This is a court of law. Justice doesn't come into it."

Shylock's supporters were grim-faced after the defeat. Although Shylock's actions can be seen as no more than a lust for revenge, they argue that the whole case underlines the prejudice of the system.

Fair Deal

"We should have known better than to try to get a fair deal out of this system," said one Jew.

"We are human beings. We bleed, we cry, we thirst. Maybe you can't fight hatred with hatred. But maybe you should also expect that the punishment is fair."

As to the final punishment – that Shylock become a Christian – there was widespread scorn.

"You can't force someone to believe," said one observer. "That's the problem with these Christians in Venice. They're about as merciful as Attila the Hun."

Portia is Lawyer

The lawyer who obtained the successful verdict is a woman, it was revealed today.
Portia (32) is engaged to Bassanio and came to Venice in disguise to defend her fiancé's friend.

She was aided in her task by her gentlewoman, Nerissa.

"I knew they'd never let me do it if they thought I was a woman," she said.

"It took a woman to defeat this disgusting Jewish dog, but you try telling that to a man. They're so bigoted."

BARD LIVING

Food, Drink, Health

Midsummer Madness

TV's Two Merry Ladies treat you to the ideal menu for an outdoor party, or a ludicrously attempted seduction.

Venison Pasty
Use only the best quality venison. You local poacher will be able to advise you on what is the best cut. Venison, of course, is always better if it is well hung. But isn't that the same for most things in life? N.B. Don't cook the horns.

Potted Coney
Coney, or rabbit, is a cheap and popular dish. Well, we get it cheap because it's always nicked from Justice Shallow's estate. For a dinner party of four, two rabbits should do. (If you need more, leave the rabbits alone for 15 minutes.)

Hodge Pudding
A local delicacy this – a boiled pudding made of the entrails of a pig. Best eaten with a blindfold on. And a peg on your nose. In fact, best not eaten at all, if we're honest.

Stewed Prunes
There has been a lot of talk about food snobbery, and looking down on simple dishes. But we say there is nothing better for someone who is stuck up than a dish of stewed prunes. We always serve this with a purée of sennapods and a dash of syrup of figs. It's sure to make your dinner party go with a dash.

Wine Seller!

This week's recommended wines from Sir John Falstaff

1595 Duke Of Clarence Malmsey
A great wine with a lot of body. A whole body, in fact. Still, too good to waste.

1620 New Canary
They tell me that this wine comes from the Canaries which is amazing. I never knew the little things were so clever. I had a parrot once but it never made anything as good as this. The only thing it did was shout "Prince Hal has a face like a baboon." In the end it was arrested. Not for libel, but for breaking the official secrets act.

Shylock's Own Kosher Brandy
Produced in Venice, this is the drink that puts the "spirit" in spiritual. Produced to conform with strict dietary laws, meaning you can get drunk with a clear conscience.

Lord de Boys' Finest Sack, 1605
My own personal tipple. Excellent straight from the pipe, or as a warmed posset, if you like your posset warm, that is.

Bard Health

Dr. Caius answers your questions

Dear Doctor,
We are two happily married women who are the subject of advances from a fat old drunkard. Is there anything we can do to him to calm him down?
Mistresses F. and P. of Windsor.

Bonjour, my little petit pois, There are all kinds of cures we could apply. A touch of bromide in his tea, perhaps, or simply getting him blind drunk as often as possible (there is every chance he does this naturally).

However I recommend teaching him a lesson. Have him visit you and then shove him in a stinky laundry basket perhaps; or get him dressed up as an old woman and thumped a lot.

After all, this is a lot more fun than bromide.

Dear Doctor,
I am a Greek procurer who has caught a 'personal' disease, if you know what I mean. Can you help me?

Yours,
Pandarus of Troy

No. Go away, you horrible little man.

Dear Doctor,
I am told I have a quotidian ague. Is this a compliment?
Yours,
Bishop of Winchester

I'm afraid not. You will probably die, raving wildly about your past crimes. Still, look on the bright side, at least we won't have to sit through any more of your sermons.

PRE-HEATED COVEN!

Wild goings on in woods around Windsor

Police are still investigating sightings of a "wild orgy" near Herne's Oak last night.

The orgy, which began on the stroke of midnight centred around a fat man in a deer costume.

"I saw this enormous monster with horns on its head," said one eyewitness. "It appeared to be fighting a load of fairies.

"At one point I heard it shouting, 'Please don't turn me into a piece of cheese.' Then everyone ran off with everyone else. Out of nowhere two older men appeared and grabbed the fairies. I reckon it was one of them there all-night raves."

Baffled

Police are said to be baffled by the mystery.

"We're not used to this kind of thing round here," said one. "This is Berkshire for heaven's sake. People don't join a coven. The nearest thing we have to a demonic organization round here is the Young Conservatives."

Interpol

The Windsor constabulary are said to be liaising with Interpol over the disturbance.

"There were some goings on with fairies in Athens a few years back," said the Chief Inspector. "We need to find out if this is all part of an international conspiracy, or just a load of middle-aged people running about and being very silly."

Brewing

Local residents say that the trouble has been brewing up for days.

"There has already been a lot of trouble around here, with people thrown into rivers and what have you," said one resident.

"The whole town is turning into a farce."

TITANIC TRIUMPHS

Titus Andronicus returns to Rome with Goth captives

Titus Andronicus, the so-called "patron of virtue" and Rome's best champion, has returned home with a load of Goths.

He has brought with him their Queen, Tamora and given instructions that her eldest boy is to be killed.

"I'm giving him to the people of Rome to be slaughtered in the streets," he said. "No, please, there's no need to thank me."

Crowned

The citizens wanted Titus to be proclaimed Emperor. Instead he's declared that Saturninus, the heir of the previous ruler, should be crowned.

"It's only right that Saturninus should be Emperor," he said. We must preserve the purity of the gene pool. Only that way can we continue to get as Emperor the type of grade A loonies we deserve."

TAMORA BOOM-DI-AY!

Emperor Chooses Queen of the Goths for his Bride

Tamora the Goth Queen has been selected by Saturninus to be his new bride. He had been expected to choose Lavinia, daughter of Titus Andronicus, but changed his mind when Lavinia was kidnapped by his brother Bassanius.

"He seemed to go off Lavinia after that," said an observer. "Instead he decided to free Tamora and marry her. It's his first nutty act of what we are hoping will be a truly loony imperial career.

"Despite the fact that Bassanius took her by force, I think he felt Lavinia didn't put up enough of a fight."

Pessimism

The move does not bode well for Titus Andronicus, who earlier in the day had sacrificed Tamora's eldest son.

"Call me Mr Pessimism," said a spokesman, "but I don't think she's likely to forget a thing like that. Certainly not when you consider it only happened this afternoon."

BASSANIUS MURDERED
Emperor's Brother Slain
Titus's Sons Arrested

Bassanius, brother of the emperor and husband of Lavinia, has been killed.

Police have arrested two men they found on the scene. The men are reported to be Quintus and Martius, the sons of Titus Andronicus.

Framed

Police discovered the boys in a pit with the body of their murdered uncle. The boys claim that they have been framed, but the police are pointing to a letter found at the scene.

"The letter outlines the whole scheme," said a police inspector. "They murdered him and hid the money in a bunch of nettles. It was a classic sting."

"They were caught red-handed," said a police spokesman. "They were in this deep ditch, with the body itself. Still, at least it saves us having to dig a grave."

Lost for Words
Lavinia assaulted in the woods
Hands and tongue amputated

In what has to be described as a pretty bad day for the Andronicus family, Lavinia, wife of Bassanius, was discovered in the woods with her hands cut off and tongue removed.

"We think she's been raped," said a policewoman. "But naturally, at the moment she's a tad upset."

She was discovered by her uncle Marcus. He rushed her to hospital, pausing only to make a 46 line speech.

"She's in a state of shock," he told reporters. "Imagine – yesterday she was happy and carefree and today – well, let's just say she'll never play the harp again. The best we can hope for her is a career in 'Give Us A Clue'."

Police have confirmed that Lavinia was mutilated to stop her telling them who did it.

"She can't write and she can't speak," they said. "So it's a bit difficult taking down a statement."

Lavinia was not available for comment.

A BIG HAND FOR THE EMPEROR

Andronicus in Bizarre Bargain

Titus Andronicus has injured himself and his brother after a message from the Emperor that his sons would be pardoned if they cut off their hands.

"He had a message saying that if he sent one of his severed hands to the Emperor, then he would return the boys to us," said Marcus. "So he cut it and sent it."

When asked if it was painful, Titus replied, "Cutting off the hand was bad enough. But wrapping it up for the post was a nightmare."

However, after all that effort, Titus was shocked to discover that his sons were returned to him in the form of severed heads.

"I can only assume it's some kind of bizarre practical joke," he said.

Aaron the Moor, a servant of the Emperor and suspected lover of the Queen, has been accused of being the perpetrator.

"I am merely the messenger," he said. "Is it my fault that everyone in Rome is keen on chopping limbs off?"

LAVINIA – POLICE INVESTIGATIONS CONTINUE

Police investigations into the rape and mutilation of Lavinia continue.

"We have discovered that it is two words, and the first word has four syllables," they said. "We did think that the whole thing was a book, a film, a stage show and a TV programme, until we discovered she was just trying to scratch her head."

Truth

However, her father Titus is certain he knows who perpetrated the crime.

"It was Demetrius and Chiron, the sons of the Queen," he said. "I know the truth. And I will be revenged."

Police were trying to calm the situation.

"We do not recommend anyone to take the law into their own hands," said a policeman. "Or stumps in Lavinia's case."

Aaron Top

Aaron confesses up a ladder

Aaron the Moor, widely considered to be one of the main culprits behind Rome's current spate of violence, has been captured.

He was caught by the invading Goth army, led by Lucius, eldest son of Titus Andronicus. Lucius began leading the army as revenge for the deaths of his brother and the savage treatment of the rest of his family.

"We found the Moor trying to hide a child he had fathered," said a soldier. "It's the first time I've ever seen him show any concern for another human being."

Ladder

Aaron admitted his guilt after being forced to climb a ladder.

"I've no idea what that was all about," said a witness. "Lucius forced Aaron to climb to the top of these steps. Aaron thought it was a gotcha at first."

Lucius explained the idea.

"The first step in any interrogation is to discover whether the accused has ever been a window cleaner," he told us. "I read that somewhere in a book."

"He's utterly mad," said Aaron. "But then they all are."

HONEY – I ATE THE KIDS

Queen's Boys Make It Into Cookery Books

Titus Andronicus was revenged on Queen Tamora today, when he served the Queen her sons at dinner.

"He killed them in revenge for what they did to Lavinia," said a family spokesman. "And then he cooked them in a pie and served them up at a banquet."

The banquet ended in a blood bath with Titus and Lavinia dead, along with Saturninus the emperor.

After being tricked into eating her children, Queen Tamora was stabbed to death.

"It was a case of eat, drink and be merry, for Tamora you die," said a waiter.

"The whole thing gives a new meaning to the phrase 'having the family round for dinner'."

Aaron Punished

Lucius, last surviving son of Titus, has been declared emperor. He has ordered state funerals for his father and sister and the late Emperor. The rest of the dead are to be thrown out for the crows.

Meanwhile Aaron the Moor is to be buried up to his neck and starved to death.

"I shouldn't think he's too bothered about that," said an observer. "Not considering what kinds of food they serve up at their meals."

VALENTINE'S DAY

Exiled Suitor Joins Rebels

The new leader of the rebels is Valentine, the young gentleman from Verona who was exiled from the Duke's court.

Valentine's crime was to fall in love with Silvia, the Duke's daughter.

"Heaven knows I'm not a snob," said the Duke, "but he's simply not our type. He hasn't got a title or anything. I'm not having my daughter elope with riff-raff."

"Upset"

Silvia is said to be "upset" by the banishment, and there are rumours that she is planning to follow Valentine into the forest.

"She is planning to meet her friends at Friar Patrick's," said a source. "I think that's a monk's cell, although it could just as easily be a chip shop."

Proteus

Meanwhile, Silvia is being wooed by Valentine's friend from Verona, Proteus.

"I hope Valentine doesn't get to hear about this," said a witness. "Proteus is supposed to be on his side. And anyway Proteus left a girl called Julia back in Verona. They were engaged.

"I only hope she hasn't disguised herself as a boy, called herself Sebastian and entered Proteus's service to spy on him.

"But then again, that would probably just be stupid."

Grabbed By The Outlaws!

Virtually everyone has been kidnapped

Silvia has been kidnapped by the outlaws, after attempting to escape from her arranged marriage.

Not only that but the Duke, Proteus, Thurio and even a small dog have been captured.

"You can't go into those woods without being grabbed by the outlaws," said an observer. "All this kidnapping is getting out of..."

He was unable to finish his sentence due to being kidnapped.

Rescued by Love

Valentine the rebel leader has rescued Silvia and been given her hand in marriage as a reward.

Meanwhile, his friend Proteus has seen the error of his ways and fallen in love with Julia again.

"I don't know what came over me," said Proteus. "I should have realized that the servant I hired was Julia all along. It was the codpiece that put me off."

Others, however, were not fooled.

"I knew it was her, the moment I saw her," said Valentine. "It wasn't a proper codpiece for a start. It was a boil-in-the-bag kipper."

BARD FASHION

Black is Out – Yellow Stockings Are In!

Yellow is the new black

That's the latest news from the fashion-frenzied world that is Illyria.

Shops throughout the province have been stocking up on stockings.

"We're doing some lovely stuff at the moment," said top designer Maria de Quant. "And yellow is very much the colour du jour. Why, only the other day we had a top court administrator here trying on a pair of our 'Wonder-leg Thunder Thigh' stockings in a very striking lemon. They were so him."

Passé

The trend is bad news for all those puritans at court who delight in the basic black.

"Black is so passé," said Maria. "They need to brighten up a bit, get a bit of colour into their lives."

According to experts, the latest trend is for cross-gartering the yellow stocking to provide an even more striking effect.

"It's very striking," said Maria. "And it shows off your lallies to lovely effect."

We spoke to one stocking convert, Malvolio, the steward of Lady Olivia. "Of course," he told us, "you've got to have the legs for it. Some people can't carry it off, but I have lovely calf muscles, don't you think?"

Ridiculous

Others were not so sure.

"I think he looks completely ridiculous," said a servant. "With those bright yellow stockings and the black cross garters he looks like a particularly confused bee."

Malvolio was unrepentant.

"They're just jealous. Some are born trendy, others achieve trendiness, some have trendiness thrust upon them. The only problem is that they cut off the blood supply. I've got feet like balloons, because the blood is having difficulty making it up my legs."

MAD-VOLIO

BARD EXCLUSIVE

Care In the Community Blamed for Steward's Incarceration

Malvolio, steward of Lady Olivia, has been imprisoned following a nervous breakdown.

"It was ghastly," said a witness. "He started grinning at her. It was like something out of the Evil Dead."

However, solicitors for the steward claim that he is not mad at all.

"This is a massive indictment of Illyria's Care in the Community policy," said Malvolio's solicitor. "My client is not mad. At worst he has been guilty of bad fashion sense. Just because he suddenly starts grinning at people doesn't mean he's mad. He might have been watching a Carry On film or something."

Awful

Eyewitnesses report how the steward behaved in a manner totally out of character.

"He was awful," said a shocked Sir Toby Belch. "I saw the man skip. He appears to think that Lady Olivia fancies him. Whereas I know for a fact that she would rather snog a dead sheep."

Malvolio, however, remained adamant that he had received a letter from Olivia promising undying love.

"It was in a code that only I could understand," he insisted, showing symptoms of what many experts believe to be classic paranoia.

Multiple Personalities

In a related incident, Cesario, the Duke's servant, has been accused of multiple personality disorder.

"One minute he's a great big girlie, the next minute he's beating me up," said an injured Sir Andrew Aguecheek. "I only challenged him to a duel because I thought he was a great big girl's blouse. But the next time we met it was like he was a different person entirely. He gave me a right going over."

Appeal

Meanwhile Malvolio has pledged that he will appeal.

"I intend to write a letter to her ladyship," he told us through the bars in his cell. "Just as soon as they let me have any light in here.

"*After all, were it not for her letter, I wouldn't be in here in the first place.*"

I NOW DECLARE YOU WIFE AND WIFE

Confusion over girl in disguise as brother and sister reunited

Confusion reigned at a society wedding today. Just for a moment it looked as though two women had got married.

The problem arose because one of the women, Viola, had disguised herself as a man.

"Things got out of hand," said Viola. "It was bad enough when she was flirting with me. But when we went out shopping and she insisted on helping me to buy underwear it got really scary."

Twin

The problem was resolved, however, by the reappearance of Sebastian, Viola's twin brother.

"Thankfully he's a man," said Viola. "So the marriage is legal."

"I'm delighted," said Olivia. "He looks just like Viola, but he shaves and wears his socks in bed. It's the best of both worlds."

Trousers

Meanwhile Viola has caught the eye of Duke Orsino.

"Heaven knows who is going to wear the trousers in their marriage," said an observer.

IT'S PARTY TIMON!

Athenian merchant holds non-stop parties for his friends

He's renowned for his generosity, loans huge sums without asking for repayment, has spent a fortune on civic projects. But how secure is his wealth?

The financial world in Athens has been rocked by a series of rumours about Timon of Athens, the multi-millionaire.

"The picture is sketchy," said one financial analyst, "but it appears that he owes huge sums to certain investors.

"We know that he owes about 25,000 crowns in cash. We also know that for the past few years he, or his steward, has been selling land and property. We have to infer that he does not have enough money to repay the debts."

Blow

If Timon is bankrupt it will strike a huge blow to the economic community, much of which has centred on selling him any number of luxuries.

"I've been selling him paintings for years," said one painter. "He always paid well and never bothered with how good the pictures were. Which is all you want out of a patron really."

Philosopher

"For years he's been surrounded by hangers-on and parasites," exclaimed his friend Apemantus, a renowned philosopher of the "Suicidal School" and author of the best-selling book, *101 Reasons Why Life Stinks*.

"I've been moaning about them for years, but he's never taken any notice. I could see it coming.

"Now it appears that he's been robbing Peter to pay Paul. I wonder if any of his so-called friends will come to his aid now?"

Timon Gentlemen Please
Timon soaks his luke-warm friends

Timon of Athens, the disgraced multi-millionaire, has thrown water over his so-called friends at a special banquet.

"It was shocking," said one. "He invited us round and we all thought it was for the usual blow-out. There were these covered dishes in front of us, but when we took the covers off there was nothing in the dishes except water.

"Then Timon went bonkers, chucking water over us all and calling us spongers and parasites."

The outburst comes in the wake of another failed rescue attempt for Timon Enterprises Inc.

"He's been to all his previous friends and they've all refused to give him dosh," said his steward. "And these people have had masses of money from him in the past. I guess he just had enough."

The assault seems to confirm reports that Timon is having some kind of nervous breakdown.

"He's lost his fortune and he's lost his faith in mankind," said his steward. "As if that weren't bad enough one of his old friends, Alcibiades, has just been exiled from Athens for asking the Senate to spare the life of a criminal."

"It's hardly surprising he's losing it. And anyway, at least going mad doesn't cost anything."

Timon Tide
Ex-millionaire moves into cave by the sea

Disgraced mogul Timon of Athens is now living in a cave by the sea, shouting at passers-by and throwing stones at anyone who annoys him.

"It's a complete collapse," said his friend Alcibiades. "He is totally disillusioned with humanity and wants nothing to do with anyone. He just chucks half-bricks at you until you go away."

Gold

But in an amazing coincidence Timon discovered treasure while he was digging up root vegetables to eat.

"He discovered gold in the ground, while he was looking for a carrot," said an eyewitness. "But he just gave it away. He's had money and it didn't do him any good.

"Now he just wants to be left alone."

UNTIL THE END OF TIMON

Timon of Athens is dead.
Only a few weeks ago he was Athens' richest man. Then the money ran out, his friends ran away and he was left alone.

He died a bitter, lonely man, sitting alone in his cave by the sea.

"His problem was he never knew the middle of humanity, just the extremes," said Apemantus. "He went from immensely rich to utterly poor; from hundreds of friends to none. No wonder he went mad."

While he has been living in the cave, the Athens that rejected him has been conquered by Alcibiades, using some of the gold that Timon found.

"I'm going to kill anyone who didn't support him," said Alcibiades. "It's what he would have wanted."

CARDINAL SINNER

Wolsey's Taxes Are the Last Straw

Cardinal Wolsey is facing strong public criticism of his new wave of taxes.

"These are the last straw," said a hard-pressed weaver. "I've got to give a sixth of my earnings to support the war in France. I wouldn't mind, but we haven't even got a war in France."

Cardinal Wolsey is adamant that the taxes are necessary.

"I agree we aren't at war with the French at the moment," he said. "But you never know when these things are going to break out. It's better to be safe than sorry."

Revoked

Now the taxes are likely to be revoked, as Katharine of Aragon has intervened on behalf of the common people.

"The King wishes the taxes to be revoked," she said. "And if he could take his mind off other women for a moment, he might be able to rein the Cardinal in a bit."

Katharine is not the only one who has questioned Cardinal Wolsey's influence at court.

"There's no doubt who's wearing the trousers," said one observer. "Or the cassock to be more precise. The Cardinal arranges everything. I wouldn't mind if he was actually doing a good job, but the peace he negotiated with France isn't working. They're still nicking all our goods."

Treason

Wolsey is also thought to have been behind the recent conviction of Buckingham on charges of treason.

"There are no doubts about this conviction," he told a packed press conference. "I know that Buckingham planned to kill the King. And me. And the Queen. And a lovely little kitten called Fluffy. That's the kind of man we're dealing with."

EXCLUSIVE

Boleyn Ball

King Henry falls for Dance Beauty

King Henry VIII has fallen in love. And the object of his affection is a young woman by the name of Anne Boleyn, or Bullen, depending on whether you can spell or not.

"The King met her at a ball arranged by Cardinal Wolsey," said a friend. "It was love at first sight. Well, actually it was lust at first sight, but the King has a problem differentiating between the two."

The liaison threatens the marriage between Henry and Katharine.

"It's probably just a seven year itch," said a friend. "But then again the King has lots of these itches. In fact he never stops scratching."

WE ARE SINGLE

King Henry divorces Katharine to marry Anne

King Henry VIII has divorced Katharine of Aragon.

The ceremony was overseen by his adviser Cranmer. He separated from his wife of 20 years on the grounds of "being King and doing what I like".

"We have discovered a loophole in the original marriage agreement," said Cranmer. "It appears that Katharine is technically Spanish and therefore nobody cares about her very much."

It is thought that the divorce has led to a split between Henry and his long-term adviser Cardinal Wolsey.

"I think Wolsey hoped that the King would marry a French Duchess," said a source. "Or maybe the Cardinal wanted to marry the King himself. Heaven knows he's had everything else."

WOLSEY IS FILED AWAY

"He was richer than I was," complained King

Cardinal Wolsey's long reign as the King's right hand man is at an end. The split came after the Cardinal accidentally left a file of personal papers amongst documents handed to the King.

The file showed that Wolsey had

- **opposed the King's divorce from Katharine**
- **amassed a huge personal fortune – greater than the King's**
- **disapproved of Henry's marriage to Anne Boleyn**
- **never had a kitten called Fluffy**
- **called the King a "great big wobble-bottom"**

"All of these are capital offences," said Cranmer. "Especially the wobble-bottom one."

The Cardinal has been committed to the Tower where he will probably be executed.

"The King lost his head over Anne Boleyn," said a courtier. "Now it looks like the Cardinal is about to join him."

CRANMER TRIUMPHS

England Rejects Rome

"Let's have a reformation," says jubilant King

In a tense and acrimonious council meeting last night, Thomas Cranmer overcame opposition to establish England as a Protestant nation.

The victory was achieved only after the King emerged from hiding to support the Archbishop.

"Before the council meeting the King gave me his support," said Cranmer. "I thought that was a bit unwieldy, so I borrowed his ring instead. When it looked like the vote was going to go against me I produced the ring and everyone knew the King was on my side. That sort of decided things."

Baptism

The King further showed his support for Cranmer by asking the Archbishop to baptize his newly-born daughter Elizabeth.

"This is a momentous day for our nation," said the King. "From now on we will have our own Church – the Church of England.

"Of course, it won't be any more effective than the last one, but at least it's ours."

Wolsey Dies

Cardinal Wolsey died a few days ago of a fever caught when travelling between different castles.

"He was being moved from London to Leicester when he caught a fever and died," said his physician. "Still, it saved him having his head cut off, I suppose."

The Cardinal will be remembered for his enormous wealth, his machiavellian scheming and his powerful influence.

Yet he will also be remembered for endowing two major colleges – one at Oxford University and the other The Cardinal Wolsey School of Finance and Accounting in Ipswich.

"He died fearing God," said his doctor. "Which is not a bad way to go, I suppose."

THOUGHT FOR THE DAY

With Cardinal Wolsey

Good morning.

You know, lately I've had more time to reflect on life.

When you are locked up in a tower awaiting death, it does tend to concentrate the mind on what really matters: friends, independence, the chances of getting hold of an oxy-acetylene bar-cutter, that sort of thing.

And I've been thinking that I never spent enough time thinking about religion. I know that some would say that, as a Cardinal, I should at least have prayed occasionally. I don't know what it was, I just always seemed to be so busy.

Conscience

Now all that has been taken away from me and I have a healthier view of life. Unfortunately I am in an unhealthy position i.e. death row, but that's not the point.

My conscience is clear. I have made peace with God.

I am trying to face my end with dignity. At the moment I can only do this by bending over and using a mirror, but with the help of some stretching exercises, I hope to get fitter.

Some people might think that I am depressed, but I choose to view this as a huge learning opportunity.

Perhaps it would be good for all of us if we were locked up and executed occasionally.

It might make us rethink our priorities in life.

NO WOMAN, NO CRY

King declares a female free zone to aid study

The King of Navarre has declared that all women are to be barred from his court. The injunction, which bans women from coming within a mile of the court, is to aid the men in their study and contemplation.

"Women are a distraction," said one of his courtiers. "We have decided to devote ourselves to study and conversation. Without them we will be more focussed. Also we'll be able to leave the toilet seat up and watch football whenever we want to."

The King has laid down rules that the court has to follow:

• **No women within a mile of the place, on pain of having their tongues cut out.**

• **Any man seen talking to a woman within three years will have to 'endure such public shame as the rest of the court can devise'. This may include chinese burns, or being flicked with a wet towel.**

• **Any man saying the word "woman" to be laughed at and openly mocked.**

• **All pictures of Claudia Schiffer will be confiscated.**

The new rules come into force with immediate effect, but already the court is having to compromise. The Princess of France is expected with her followers next week.

"Obviously we will make an exception in her case," said a spokesman. "Partly because she is a wise and witty woman. But mainly because her Dad is the King and if we didn't speak to her he would mash us to pieces.

"There are some things more important than study, you know."

Costard In The Jug

Following an unauthorized meeting with a female, Costard the Clown has been put in prison.

He was found guilty of conversing with Jaquenetta, a country girl from a local farm.

His punishment will be a week's diet of bran and water.

"I suppose I should be grateful," he said. "It could have been the wet towels. But it was worth it just to talk to Jaquenetta."

Ask Auntie Bard

Your questions answered by our very own Agony Auntie

Dear Auntie Bard,

I am in love with a girl called Rosaline. Despite the fact that she spends all her time mocking me, I think she likes me as well. The problem is, I am not allowed to talk to girls unless the Duke says so. What should I do?

Yours,
Berowne
P.S. I have known her for four days and she has not yet shown any inclination to dress up in boys' clothing. Is this normal?

Dear Berowne,

Well, this is a tricky one. Frankly there are only three options:
1) Elope with her and run a long way away,
2) Claim that you had your fingers crossed when you took the vow of celibacy,
3) Hope that the Duke falls for a woman too.

And don't worry about the lack of cross-dressing. I'm sure she'll get round to it sooner or later. They always do.
All the best
Auntie Bard

Dear Auntie Bard,

I am in love with the Princess of France. The problem is, I am not allowed to talk to girls unless the Duke says so. And I am the Duke. What should I do?
Yours,
Duke of Navarre

Dear Duke,

Oh for heaven's sake. Get a grip, man.
All the best
Auntie Bard

Dear Auntie Bard,

Maria. I've just seen a girl called Maria. And suddenly I find I want to hold her hand and generally smother her with passion. The problem is, I am not allowed to talk to girls unless the Duke says so. What should I do?
Yours,
Longaville

Dear Longaville,

This is getting stupid.
All the best
Auntie Bard

Dear Auntie Bard,

I am in love with the most divine Kate...etc, etc.
Yours,
Dumaine

Dear Dumaine,

Don't tell me, you can't talk to her, you've taken a vow.

Now look, you lot. Why don't you ring the bell and see if Mr Real is at home?

Drop this silly nonsense about not talking to women. They won't bite, you know. Well, not unless the relationship goes particularly well.
All the best
Auntie Bard

Dear Auntie Bard,

BUT WE'VE TAKEN A VOW!
Yours,
Duke, Berowne, Longaville, Dumaine

Dear All,

Do I look like I care?

Can we move onto another topic now?
All the best
Auntie Bard

Dear Auntie Bard,

I am in love with Jaquenetta. The problem is I am called Costard the Clown. Should I change my name to something more exciting? Like Coco, perhaps? Or Charlie? What do you think.
Yours,
Costard

Dear Costard,

I think you should all go away and leave me alone.
Get lost
Auntie Bard

THE KING IS DEAD
Year's vow for lovers

The King of France is dead.

News reached the court at Navarre yesterday, interrupting the ball that was in progress and bringing a chill wind of reality to the proceedings.

The Princess is due to return to the court today.

In the meantime, the young lovers who were tortuously cementing their relationships have reached an agreement.

The men, who vowed to do without women and then fell head over heels in love with the first lot who appeared, will have to spend a year apart.

"It's not that we want them to suffer," said the Princess. "Well, all right, we do want them to suffer a bit actually."

Among the courtiers Berowne, who is famous for never taking anything seriously, will have to spend a year visiting dying patients in hospitals.

"I think this is a bit cruel," said a doctor. "I mean, haven't these people suffered enough?"

KATHARINE OF ARROGANT

Merchant's Daughter wins "Shrew of the Year Award" Again

Katharine Minola has been crowned "Shrew of the Year" in Padua's annual "woman you'd least like to be married to" competition.

The award makes it four years in a row for Katharine. Previous to that she was six times winner of the "Most Horrific Adolescent" prize.

"We're incredibly proud of her," said her coach, a small, prematurely bald, harassed looking man. "Admittedly we haven't told her about the award. She'd only throw it at us."

End

However, there are signs that Katharine's reign may soon be at an end.

Petruchio, the All-Italy Open Woman Taming Champion, has declared his love for Kate and his ambition to marry her.

"When I told her about it, she screamed, swore, insulted me, told me to get lost and finally threw a set of crockery at me.

"I'm very encouraged by the response."

Relief

The news of Petruchio's interest will come as a welcome relief to Bianca, Katharine's sister. She has been unable to marry before her sister was hitched.

"We've tried everything," she said. "We've tried pleading with potential suitors, threatening them with injury, or even bribing them. But it's no good. None of them want to go near her."

Motives

"Others, however, have expressed doubts about Petruchio's motives.

"I can't tell if he actually loves her, or if he's just interested in the money," said a friend.

"He's desperate for cash, and desperate men do dangerous things.

"Mind you, he'd have to be more than desperate to marry Kate for money. He'd have to be barking mad as well."

Hanged

When asked if she was going to marry Petruchio, Katharine beat up the reporter and broke his camera. She then shouted, "I'll see him hang'd first."

Petruchio was unconcerned.

"It's an improvement," he said. "Last time she said she wanted to see me disembowelled and then hung.

"I think she's thawing."

FRIGHT WEDDING

The Wedding from Hell for Petruchio and Kate

Petruchio has married his "Kate" in a marriage as bizarre as their courtship.

"He walked up the aisle in the most ragged, motley assortment of clothes you could imagine," said a member of the congregation. "You should have seen her face. If looks could kill he'd have been leaving that church in a coffin."

But the wedding got worse. Guests gazed in amazement as Petruchio

- **hit the vicar**
- **swore at the congregation**
- **threw wine over the sexton**
- **behaved like a tramp**
- **gave Kate a kiss so loud that it echoed round the walls**

"Katharine was so shocked she was lost for words," said a family friend. "And believe me, that's shocked."

Tantrums

"It was like seeing two toddlers trying to out-tantrum each other," said another friend. "Petruchio is trying a 'kill or cure' policy. He thinks that by being more outrageous than Katherine she will realize what she is like."

The Vicar remained diplomatic.

"He's a loud-mouthed bully with the manners of a chimpanzee," said the Rev. Sebastian Chasuble. "And she's a monster with a tongue sharper than a razor blade.

"I think they are ideally matched."

Petruchio Faces Lawsuit

Tailor Sues over "Time Wasting"

A tailor employed to make a dress for Mrs Petruchio is to sue.

"I made the dress according to very specific instructions," he said. "But when I took it round, Petruchio tore it to pieces."

The tailor claims that Mrs Petruchio, née Katharine Minola, really liked the dress.

"It was a very tense meeting," he reported. "Everything she liked he wouldn't let her have."

Now he is to sue for malicious time wasting.

"I'm a creative artist, I am," he told us. "I've been called the Nureyev of the Needle. You've no idea what rejection I feel."

KISS ME KATE

Petruchio and Kate are reconciled in the street

Following a tumultuous few days of married life, Petruchio and Kate sealed their relationship with a loving and very public kiss.

"They stood in the main street and snogged," said a witness. "I can remember a time when Kate would have died first. But there does seem to be something between them."

In the few days that they have been wed, Katharine has been half-starved, thrown into mud, and dressed in the plainest of clothes. Yet now she obeys him and talks quietly and calmly.

Changed

Indeed, so changed is she, that Petruchio won a substantial bet with fellow new husbands over whose wife would come quickest when they called. Kate not only came quickly, she even gave a speech extolling the virtues of womanly submission.

"It was amazing," said a fellow guest at the banquet. "She talked about her husband as Lord, as head, as sovereign. I think she was serious as well.

"Of course, if she was being ironic, then Petruchio is in a lot of trouble."

Kate Brainwashed
Women's group call for action

A feminist group have called for action over Petruchio's treatment of his new bride.

"This isn't taming, it's breaking," said a spokesman for the Official Veronese Unity Meeting (OVUM). "She has been physically weakened into submission."

Defeated

"She may well have changed her behaviour. But how much of that is because of their relationship, and how much is because she has been defeated is open to debate."

Experts dismissed their claims.

"Firstly, Kate can give as good as she gets," said her father Baptista. "Secondly, I think Petruchio has changed as well. He's less detached and cynical. He might have taught her manners, she might have taught him how to feel."

"*Thirdly, and most importantly, this is sixteenth century Italy. So nobody gives a monkeys what a load of women think.*"

THE CLEAN MACHINE

New deputy aims to clean up the city

Angelo has been appointed Deputy to Duke Vincentio. And he's already declared his aim to clean up the city of Vienna.

"This place has become a moral black hole," he said at a packed press conference. "The Duke has gone away for a while and left me in charge. And I intend to do something about it."

Although detailed arrangements have not yet been released, Angelo plans to:

- **Close all the brothels**
- **Increase censorship laws**
- **Execute anybody found guilty of fornication**
- **Bring in mandatory clod showers for all unmarried men**
- **Force all women to wear hats and very large bloomers**
- **Ban all albums by The artist formally known as Duke**

"These orders will take place with immediate effect," he said. "In fact, we have already arrested our first offender – Claudio, who has got a young woman pregnant."

Claudio claims that he intends to marry the girl. However, his pleas have met with no response from Angelo.

"It's too late for that. He should have thought about that before they both... you know... thingied."

Claudio's family is expected to appeal for his pardon. His sister Isabella is due to meet the Deputy Duke tomorrow.

New Hangman Appointed

A new assistant hangman has been appointed to help clear up the backlog of cases caused by the new Deputy.

Pompey, previously a tapster at the "Marks and Slappers" Bawdy House, has been brought in to double the staff capacity.

"We are simply responding to customer demand," said the Head of the Hanging Regulatory Body, OFFHANG. "We have signed up a new customer charter which says that everyone will be hanged within three days of their conviction."

Many prisoners are complaining about the service already.

"The service is appalling," said Barnadine, a convicted murderer. "I have even been asked to stand in for someone so that they can pretend he has been hanged when he hasn't. I refused point blank. I'm not ready to die. I need more time to prepare myself. About seventy years should be enough."

THE NUN'S TALE

Did Angelo Ask Isabella for Sex? Did Duke's Deputy Promise Pardon for Pornography?

Rumours are increasing that Angelo, the so called "clean-up kid", is guilty of sexual harassment.

The rumours centre around Isabella, sister of the convicted Claudio. Sources in Vienna claim that Angelo promised to release Claudio if Isabella slept with him.

"At the very least this is rank hypocrisy," said a court official. "Let us not forget this is the guy who came in on a platform of moral responsibility and family values. Now it seems he might not be as pure as he claims."

Denial

Angelo has denied the allegations.

"I am totally innocent of all wrong-doing," he said. "This is a plot by my political enemies to bring me down. I tell you I have never had sexual relations with this woman. No, really. Cross my heart and hope to die."

Despite his protestations, the rumours refuse to go away.

"Angelo has a long history of ill-treating women," claimed one opponent. "Only five years ago he promised to marry a girl and backed out at the last moment."

Investigations

Government investigators have already been appointed to look into the scandal. The team will be led by Friar Lodowick, who will interview all participants.

"This is not a witch hunt," said the Friar, in a voice which bore an uncanny resemblance to that of the absent Duke.

"This is merely an attempt to get at the truth. I will be issuing a full report on the internet, just as soon as anyone invents it."

GUILTY!
Angelo Accused in Final Friar Report
"I may have misled you," admits leader

The Friar Report has concluded that Angelo is guilty of misusing the office of Deputy.

After examining the evidence, Friar Lodowick and his team of investigators have concluded that the Deputy did indeed put pressure on Isabella to have "un-nunlike relations with him".

Marianna

However, the report also concludes that Angelo did not actually sleep with Isabella. Instead he slept with Marianna, a woman he was previously engaged to.

"It was very dark in that vineyard," said the Deputy. "I couldn't tell who it was. Not that I'm admitting anything, mind you."

In a further damning indictment, the report shows how the Deputy reneged on his promise to free Claudio and had the prisoner executed anyway.

Scathing

Isabella was scathing in her condemnation of Angelo.

"He is a murderer, an adulterous thief, a hypocrite and a virgin-violator," she said. "And those are just his good points."

Nevertheless she has stopped short of calling for his death.

"If it was wrong to condemn my brother, it is wrong to condemn Angelo," she said.

"*We should not use justice for revenge, even though it might be a laugh.*"

FRIAR REPORT

Those findings in brief

• **Angelo met with Isabella in his private office and asked her to have sex with him, promising that her brother would be released.**

• **Eventually she agreed, arranging for her place to be taken by Marianna.**

• **Angelo and this fake "Isabella" met in the vineyard and had sex.**

• **Angelo still ordered Claudio to be hanged.**

"We find that the Deputy is guilty as charged. He has misled the city and lied about his conduct. We recommend impeachment, or maybe death. Yes, now that I come to think about it, definitely death."

Return

The Duke is due to return tomorrow. And he'll be greeted by a massive political crisis.

"I think everything will work out OK," said the Friar, who is still sounding uncannily like the Duke. "I expect he will arrange for Marianna to be married to Angelo, reveal that Claudio was not hanged, but only a dead pirate who looked like him, and then the Duke will probably marry Isabella.

"It's the obvious way out if you ask me."

TALK TALK

Beatrice denies love-match with Benedick

"He won't shut up," she claims

Beatrice has spoken out for the first time about rumours of an attraction between her and visiting soldier Benedick.

"It's all a load of nonsense," she said. "I mean, he just won't shut up. He prattles on and on."

Scathing

Benedick was equally scathing.

"The words 'pot' and 'kettle' spring to mind," he said. "She has a tongue so sharp you could slice bread with it."

Friends, however, have not given up on getting the two of them together.

"It's sort of a project of ours," said Don Pedro. "We'd like to see these two together. It's a family thing, know what I mean? No one can say we don't relish a challenge."

Power Struggle

Don Pedro is resting after a power struggle between him and his brother Don John. According to Leonato – the Godfather – the two sides appear to have made up.

"Don Pedro has pardoned Don John," said Leonato. "These things happen. You know, one day you're all friends, the next day you're lining up your brother's men against the wall and machine gunning them down. It's part of family life."

Forgiven

"This is not a time for bearing grudges," said Don John. "As far as I'm concerned it's all forgiven and forgotten. Now it's time to think about romance. I just can't wait for Saint Valentine's Day."

Crimewatch Sicily
Featuring Constable Dogberry and the City Watch

Evenin' All,

At this time of year, with returning soldiers having nothing more to do than sit around being witty, there's a lot of petty crime about. Such as pick-pockets, forged letters and people staging fake affairs in order to prevent marriages.

So my advice is, find yourself a useful occupation. After all, the devil finds work, and all that. Take up volleyball, or crochet, or exchanging barbed insults.

Meanwhile, we are still looking for the following known villains. If you know of anyone matching these descriptions, please contact the incident room.

WANTED

For murder of two curly-haired little princes
Name: Not known
Description: Male, Caucasian, hump-backed, withered arm, maniacal cackle. May well run about looking for horses.

WANTED

For murder of mother and all her children
Name: "The Scottish Man"
Description: Male, Scottish, possibly royal.
Police psychologists say he may well have an obsessive interest in horoscopes and, quite probably, a wife who is a complete loony.
Approach with caution.

WANTED

For highway robbery
Name: The Masked Mountainside
Description: Enormous bloaty with a stomach the size of Ben Nevis. Goes under the pseudonym of "The Fat Man" – an understatement if ever I heard one. Probably drunk.
Police warning: If approached, do not lend money to this man.

WANTED

For contravention of the Health and Safety in the Kitchen Act
Name: Titus "Mine's a Battered Sausage" Andronicus
Description: Large, battle-scarred, probably wearing a toga. Left hand missing.
(Might have replaced it with a hook and be chased by a crocodile. It's the kind of thing these villains get up to.)

WANTED

For scheming against happy marriages
Name: Don "The Knife" John
Description: Young, sullen, Sicilian. Part of the Don Pedro family. Might be wearing a big hat and carrying a lute case.

BACK FROM THE DEAD

Hero recovers to marry Claudio

Don John on the run following failed plot

Hero, daughter of Godfather Leonato, is alive and well, following a death scare at her wedding.

The event took place as she was preparing to marry Claudio, from the Don Pedro family.

"Instead of saying 'I do', he didn't," said a witness. "He accused her of unfaithfulness and of sleeping with someone else. She just collapsed."

"I thought she was dead," said Claudio. "I realized then I might have made a big mistake."

Duel

Members of the family immediately took sides. Beatrice, Hero's best friend, told her new man Benedick to prove his love by challenging Claudio to a duel.

"The situation could have got nasty," said Leonato. "Luckily we found a squealer called Borachio and 'persuaded' him to tell us all about the plot."

Borachio revealed that the whole thing was a fraud staged by Don John, to spite Claudio. For many it's the final straw in their relationship with the young Don.

Wrong

"I don't understand what's wrong with the boy," said his elder brother. "He's had the best education money can buy. I've always provided him with pizza, pastrami, Frank Sinatra records. What more could a Sicilian ask for?"

Now Don John is on the run. But Leonato has no doubt he will be captured.

Family

"You can't escape the family," he said. "We have 'relatives' everywhere. But he needn't worry. When he comes back I'm sure we can find a suitable position for him. Probably as part of a flyover."

The day ended with Claudio marrying a revived Hero and Benedick marrying Beatrice.

"It's a great day," said Don Pedro. "Go on, celebrate. Have some lasagne. Enjoy yourself."

THREE QUEENS TRUMP A PAIR

"Let us bury our dead" plead bereaved wives

The marriage ceremony of Hippolyta and Theseus was interrupted today by three foreign Queens on a mercy mission.

The strangers implored King Theseus to postpone his wedding and fight King Creon of Thebes.

Creon

"We three Queens of Orient are," said one Queen to a packed news conference. "Creon killed our husbands, but has refused to let us go and bury them. Needless to say, the crows think it's Christmas."

When asked if this didn't expose their husband's souls to torment, the Queen replied, "Yes, and every other part of their body as well."

Monster

The King immediately postponed his wedding and went to war with Creon.

"The time has come to deal with this monster," said Theseus. "The Creon writing is on the wall."

The three Queens planned to return to their land.

"We may have to go and follow a star first, of course," they advised.

Stop Press: Victory Confirmed

Theseus has defeated Creon and allowed the Queens to go and bury their husbands.

"We shall return with some prisoners," he confirmed. "But their stories will have to be told by another dramatist. We just don't have any more time."

PEACE TREATY

Peace Deal between Montague and Capulet

Two of the most powerful aristocratic houses in the city of Verona have signed a unique peace deal.

The deal was brokered by the Prince of Verona. It is intended to bring to an end the violence and disorder that has plagued the city.

"These two families have got to get their houses in order," said the Prince. "Otherwise, someone is going to get hurt."

To seal the agreement Old Capulet has agreed that his daughter Juliet will marry the Prince's son, Paris.

"I'm very excited by the prospect," said Juliet. "Who is he again?"

The match will be celebrated at a masked ball tonight to which Montagues and Capulets will be invited.

Security

"Naturally there will have to be some security arrangements," said the Prince. "All swords, knives, knuckledusters, clubs, CS canisters and hand grenades will have to be left at the door."

"I am sure it will be a fine celebration of a new era," said Old Capulet. "We'll have fine music, good wine and a lot of young people together. What could possibly go wrong?"

Night Lights Needed

A Verona city councillor is calling for better street lighting after overhearing a conversation between a young couple.

"It was quite clear that the girl couldn't see a thing," said Councillor Bandell. "She was saying, 'Is that you down there?' or something like that.

"If we'd had proper lighting she'd have known exactly wherefore art the bloke down below."

Keep It Quiet

A complaint has been made to the Prince about teenagers shouting to each other in the early hours of the morning.

"They went on and on," said Mrs Ethel Fluffyhat, of 39 Cymbeline Villas. "First the lad was shouting about which way east was and the suns and all that. Then he climbed up her trellis.

"He said, 'with love's light wings I did o'erperch these walls,' but he didn't. He used a ladder. I saw it."

She added, "Things were simpler in my day. If you wanted a girl you just ran off into the woods."

BARD BABE

© 1997 Louisa Hare

But soft, what light from yonder page breaks? It is the east and Juliet is the sun.

At 13, this Veronese Venus has the whole of Italy at her feet. A big Bard welcome to this week's babe –

Juliet Capulet

Yes, dawning Juliet is already turning heads. The Prince's son Paris is plighting his troth to her. And if you've got a troth you can see why it ought to be plighted!

Juliet (32-26-30) won't be around forever. In a few days time she'll be a married girl, locked away with nothing but the odd lute and a couple of tapestries to keep her company.

So enjoy her while you can - free in the pages of your brilliant, babe-tastic BARD!

Partying Is Such Sweet Sorrow

Romeo upset at ball

The ball to celebrate the impending marriage of Juliet to Paris left at least one young man more gloomy than anything else.

"Why should young girls be forced to marry just to seal a treaty?" said young Romeo Montague. "I think she should be allowed to make her own choice. I mean she is nearly 14 after all."

Outburst

The outburst came as Romeo was leaving the party where he had, by all accounts, met Juliet for the first time.

"She's gorgeous," he said. "The night hangs on her cheek like a great big night hanging thing."

"Don't tell the Prince, but I managed a quick snog when no-one was looking."

Romeo, Out You Go

Romeo exiled from Verona

Mercutio and Tybalt Dead

Romeo Montague has been exiled from Verona following a fatal fight with Tybalt, cousin of Juliet Capulet.

Details are hazy, but it appears that young Romeo was trying to pacify the suituation when it all went wrong.

"Originally Tybalt appeared and tried to pick a fight with Romeo," said Benvolio, who saw the whole thing. "When he refused to fight, Tybalt fought with Mercutio instead. Romeo tried to get in between them and stop it. But as he held him, Tybalt stabbed Mercutio."

Although Tybalt ran off, he returned later. By this time Romeo was ready to revenge his friend's death.

"Tybalt came back and Romeo fought him and killed him. I think he felt responsible for Mercutio's death," said Benvolio.

Exiled

The Prince decided that Romeo should be exiled from Verona.

"He's devastated," said Benvolio.

"He keeps on about his wife, but I know for a fact he isn't married. I don't know where he's gone tonight, but the state he's in I don't know what he'll do."

Wherever Romeo has gone, he will have to leave Verona tomorrow morning or die.

"It's not the end of the world," said his father. "He'll probably enjoy it in Mantua. Maybe he'll find a nice girl and settle down."

WEDDING DIE

Juliet dies on the day of her marriage

Juliet Capulet has died – on the very day that she was due to marry Paris, the Prince's son.

"I can't understand it," sobbed a distraught Nurse. "She was fine when she went to bed. She even seemed to be looking forward to today. Which was odd, because previously she hadn't been at all keen."

The body has been taken to the Capulet family tomb.

Baffled

Doctors are baffled as to the cause of death.

"It's weird," said one. "It almost looks as though she is sleeping. And yet I can't find a pulse or anything."

Blow

The news came as a bitter blow to Prince Escalus and his wife. They had been hoping to welcome the girl to their family.

"We were looking forward to welcoming a new daughter-in-law," said the Prince. "Now we've been left with just our son. Ah well, I suppose whatever happens we'll always have Paris."

Leprosy Causes Postal Delay

An outbreak of leprosy between Verona and Mantua is severely disrupting traffic and causing delays to post.

"There is a plague in both our houses," said the Italian Travel Centre. "All letters and parcels will have to be thoroughly disinfected before proceeding. So if you have any urgent letters outlining bizarre stratagems to fake death, then you'd be better off finding an alternative route."

TRAGEDY OF ERRORS

Juliet and Romeo
United In Death
Paris Killed At Tomb
Secret Wedding

As dawn rose in Verona today it revealed a shocking scene. Romeo and Juliet were both dead, and along with them Paris, son of the Prince.

As the bodies were taken away, details emerged of an astonishing secret marriage between the two teenagers. Of a letter that went astray. And of a plan that went badly wrong.

Married

"Romeo and Juliet were married," said Friar Laurence, who revealed the truth behind the tragedy. "She was playing dead to avoid marrying Paris, but the letter explaining the plan to Romeo never got there."

The young Montague returned to Verona. There he surprised Paris at the the tomb and killed him in a fight. Then, believing his young wife dead, Romeo took poison.

Mix-Up

"Juliet came out of her trance, saw her husband lying there and stabbed herself," explained the Friar. "It's a terrible, tragic mix up."

"I blame myself. Although not as much as I blame the Montagues and the Capulets."

Learn

"We must all learn from this," said a distraught Prince. "From now on the houses must learn to live in peace. So many young people have died and for what? A pointless squabble between two factions. All because we could not work out our differences.

"*It's just so sad.*"

The Bard "Write Your Own Sonnet and Song" Competition

Winning Entries

We had a bumper response to our Sonnet and Song competition – here are just a few excerpts from the many hundreds of entries.

Shall I compare thee to a summer's day?
Thou art more lovely and more temperate
Weather-wise, you've got a lovely warm front,
And I prefer you to Margate.

Mr. Fletcher, Rotherhithe

Fear no more the heat o' the sun
Nor the furious winter's rages;
Thou thy worldly task has done
Home art gone and ta'en thy wages
Golden lads and girls agree
I've just won the lottery.

J. Webster, London

My mistress eyes do nothing like the Sun
No, she prefers the Guardian.

Beaumont & Fletcher, Solicitors and
Commissioners of Oaths

When that I was and a little tiny boy
With a hey, ho the wind and the rain;
A foolish thing was but a toy,
For the rain it raineth every day.

And as I grew all poxy wet
With a hey, ho, by minute and hour,
I realized to my great regret,
That I was living in the bathroom shower.
Sing, hey nonny, nonny, oh stuff it.

B. Jonson, London

Where the bee sucks there suck I
In a cowslips bell I lie
No wonder I've got a bad back.

T. Kyd, Barcelona

Full fathom five thy father lies
Of his bones does coral make
That's what happens when you capsize
On the municipal boating lake.

C. Marlowe, Deptford (Deceased)

BOAR-ED TO DEATH

Adonis Dies In Hunting Accident

"He should never have rejected me," sobs jilted Goddess of Love

Adonis (18), the dimpled darling of the Greek world, is dead. He was gored by a wild boar when a hunting expedition went tragically wrong.

Among his many female mourners is Venus, Goddess of Love (immortal) who is known to have been obsessed with the boy.

"It was incredible," said a close friend. "She was all over him. It was like watching all-in wrestling. Or all-out in her case. She's never been one to hide her assets if you know what I mean."

Rejection

The Greek pin-up rejected the goddess however.

"He didn't want anything to do with her," said the friend. "She dragged him to the ground but he managed to run away.

"I think he was more put off by her passion than turned on. The irony is that if he'd given into her he would never have gone hunting. He probably wouldn't have had the energy for one thing."

Adonis was only dissuaded from filing a claim for sexual harassment by the fact that his attacker was a Greek goddess.

"You should never try to sue a resident of Olympus," advised a solicitor. "If they lose the case they're likely to turn you into a tree or a deer or something."

Death

Although the police have not released the body, Doctors have spoken of the manner of the death.

"He was gored in a particularly horrible place," said a doctor. "And I don't mean Romford. Let's just say that even had he lived, he wouldn't have been much use to her."

Sorrow

Venus, however, is inconsolable.

"Love is always mixed with sorrow," she said in a statement. "It makes the young old, and the old become a child.

"And, speaking as the Goddess of Love, I ought to know."

SEXTUS MANIAC!
Prince on rape charge
Mystery suicide of Roman woman

Prince Sextus Tarquinius has fled the city of Rome following a charge of rape. He stands accused of assaulting Lucrece, wife of Collatine. She has since committed suicide.

"Naturally we're investigating the claims," said a member of the Roman police force, "but since the whole statement runs to 265 stanzas it's taking a bit of time."

Carried Away

The incident appears to have taken place at the family estate of Collatium where Lucrece was entertaining the Prince.

"It appears he got carried away," said a friend. "I think he knew the enormity of what he was doing, but he did it just the same."

Lucrece was so shamed by the event that she stabbed herself with a knife, but not before she told her husband and other leading Romans what had happened.

Republic

They have since driven the Prince from the city, and with him the last traces of the Roman royal family.

"It is no good Tarquinius trying to claim diplomatic immunity on the grounds that he is a Prince," said an ashen-faced Collatine. "From now on, Rome will be a republic."

Phoenix and Turtle in Death Pact

Police are investigating a bizarre suicide pact between a Phoenix and a Turtle.

"It's a turtle-dove actually," explained a vet. "I mean you'd never get a Phoenix falling in love with a real turtle. That's just silly."

"The two appear to have burned themselves to death," confirmed a police spokesman. "Which is not easy for a Phoenix, being as how they always rise from the ashes."

"It was the only way they could be together," explained an ornithologist. "They are united in death."

Police are treating the death as allegorical.

MORE PLEASE

SPECIAL REPORT

Sir Thomas quells riot with his Oratory

Sir Thomas More has calmed an angry mob with a moving oration.

Sir Thomas was speaking at the annual May-Day riot, where he was facing an angry mob demanding cheaper food and better herrings.

"It's not easy being a commoner in today's society," said a mob leader. "I mean, have you seen the price of butter these days? Elevenpence a pound, mate, and that's not even spreadable straight from the fridge."

Hierarchy

The mob was calmed by the virtuous Thomas, with a description of society's hierarchy.

"I merely explained to them the way society should operate," said Sir Thomas. "At the top is God. Then the King, then the nobility, then the gentlemen, and so on, and so on, until we get right down to Jeremy Beadle and the Teletubbies.

"Therefore, in rising against the King, these people were rising against God."

Impressed

The rebels were impressed with the cleric's arguments.

"Whatever you say about him, he's got a lovely way with words," said one listener. "And there's no doubt that the rhetoric in this scene has been far better than that in Act Three."

My Labour's Lost
Playwright complains about lost plays

A leading playwright has had his first folio broken into and several plays stolen.

"I was just getting them ready for publication, when I had to pop downstairs to check on my elderly wife. While I was out, someone stole two plays."

The manuscripts, *Love's Labour's Won* and *Cardenio*, have probably been sold to collectors.

"Oh well, I expect they'll turn up some day," said the playwright. "It's not as if I'm famous or anything."

DO YOU KNOW THIS MAN?

Wanted for Forgery & Plagiarism

25 year career of bad jokes, ropey plots and bad spelling revealed

He's one of the country's top playwrights. But for the past 25 years he has been nicking all his plots from back issues of The Bard.

"I'm shocked," said a stunned editor. "It appears that he has just lifted everything from our pages – characters and all."

The playwright – who cannot be named for legal reasons – did not deny that he had "borrowed" many of his plots. "As another fine artist will one day say," he predicted, "good artists imitate, great artists steal."

Authorities

The authorities are currently looking into the situation.

"He may well be guilty on a number of counts," said an official from the Office of Fair Writing. "For a start, some of his plots have holes big enough to drive a coach through. Secondly, some of his jokes have not worn well. Thirdly, his spelling is appealing. Sorry – appalling."

Genius

However, the authorities look unlikely to press charges.

"The problem is, he's a genius," said the official. "And there is simply no accounting for them. I just hope that future generations learn to enjoy him, rather than endure him."

Aristocrat

Indeed, so great is the talent of the author, that many have found it impossible to believe he came from humble origins in Stratford-upon-Avon.

"I can't believe he isn't an aristocrat," said J. Thomas Looney. "In my opinion he's Edward de Vere the Earl of Oxford. Somebody posh, anyway."

In answer to these claims, the author merely smiled.

"As one of my characters once remarked, I am who I am," he said. "Just deal with it."

BARD BACK ISSUES

Looking for more background to our stories? Here's where you find it.

Plays By Shakespeare

All's Well That Ends Well 101
Antony and Cleopatra 13–15
As You Like It, 40, 103–5
Comedy of Errors 94–6
Coriolanus 16–20
Cymbeline 41, 91–3
Hamlet 85–90
Henry IV pt 1 54–6
Henry IV pt 2 57–9
Henry V 60–4
Henry VI pt 1 64–7
Henry VI pt 2 68–72
Henry VI pt 3 73–7
Henry VIII 123–5
Julius Caesar 7–12
King John 36–9
King Lear 21–4
Love's Labour's Lost 126–8
Macbeth 31–5
Measure for Measure 132–4
The Merchant of Venice 41, 108–10
The Merry Wives of Windsor 111–12
A Midsummer Night's Dream 25–6
Much Ado About Nothing 135–7
Othello 27–30
Pericles, Prince of Tyre 97–100
Richard II 51–3
Richard III 78–9, 82–3
Romeo and Juliet 139–143
The Taming of the Shrew 129–131
The Tempest 42–5
Timon of Athens 121–2
Titus Andronicus 113–16
Troilus and Cressida 106–7
Twelfth Night 40, 118–120
The Two Gentlemen of Verona 117
The Winter's Tale 47–50

Plays Partly Written By Shakespeare

The Two Noble Kinsmen 138
Sir Thomas More 147

Poems and Sonnets

Various 144
The Rape of Lucrece 146
The Phoenix and the Turtle 146
Venus and Adonis 145

Lost Plays

Cardenio 147
Love's Labours Won 147

Also available from HarperCollins by Nick Page

THE TABLOID BIBLE

How would the press of its day have covered the greatest story ever told?
Read all about it in *The Scroll* – the only paper that was there.

Inside your supersonic Scroll:

WOULD YOU ADAM AND EVE IT!
Scandal as couple evicted from garden

ARKING MAD!
Nutty Noah builds the world's biggest boat in his garden. "I'm sure he
doesn't have planning permission," says irate neighbour.

TOWER OF BABEL COLLAPSES
"Xxyshhibbothuth mi varg," says suddenly incomprehensible builder.

ATISHOO! ATISHOO! WALL FALL DOWN!
Insurers refuse payouts over Jericho wall collapse.
"Aggressive trumpet playing is not covered," they say.

5,000 FED WITH LOAVES AND FISHES
Miracle? Or just very thinly sliced? You decide!

KEEP IT SIMPLE
(and get more out of life)

This book is for anyone who wants a less complicated life.
It will help you to:

- deal with money
- simplify your possessions
- recognize your own priorities
- budget your time
- find space for quietness
- shape your own rule of life

If you want to live more simply, if you want to create space for
what is really important in your life, then this friendly, funny
and thought-provoking book is for you.